Just Imagine

A Life without Illness

Michael O'Doherty

with Tara King

BLACKWATER PRESS

D1208436

Text written and compiled by: Tara King

Illustrator: Bridget Dowty/Graham-Cameron Illustration

ISBN 978-0-9563541-3-6

© Blackwater Press, 2009

BWP Ltd., 1 Great Denmark Street, Dublin 1.

Printed in the Republic of Ireland.

I want to dedicate this book to my late father Michael O'Doherty, to the late Derek Dunne, journalist and ghostwriter of our first book, and to Stephen Griffin, brother of Tom Griffin, for their hard work and the energy they expended in the early stages of the development of Plexus Bio-Energy. Without their input, we would not be where we are today.

Contents

Acknowledgements .... *v*

Foreward .... *vii*

Preface .... *viii*

Testimony of Michael Flatley .... *xi*

CHAPTER 1   My Journey 1

CHAPTER 2   Grief 20

CHAPTER 3   The Clinic 34

CHAPTER 4   Disease: A Natural Reaction to an
              Unnatural State of Affairs 49

CHAPTER 5   Emotions 67

CHAPTER 6   Children's Health 83

CHAPTER 7   Cancer 97

CHAPTER 8   Your Own Personal Plan:
              Diet and Medication 126

CHAPTER 9   The Consciousness Shift 141

Acknowledgements

To my wife Tina for all her hard work and patience in making my dreams a possibility; to my mother Phyllis and my family for their ongoing support; to Tom Griffin, co-founder of Plexus, and his wife Martina Griffin for coming into my life and giving me this possibility; to my wife's parents Nancy and Jamsie and her brother James for their support; to George Canning of Mugendo Kickboxing and Zdenko Domančić for his generosity and making it all possible for us; to Bridget Ruane researcher of *The Late Late Show* in 1990 and of course Gay Byrne for the opportunity and the exposure; to Paddy and Bride Walsh from Kiltimagh, County Mayo for their support in the beginning and the Donovan family in Newcastle West.

To all journalists from the print media, radio and TV, both national and international, of which there are too many to mention, thank you for your time and the ongoing exposure of our system because if it were not for you many people would not have been able to experience better health. To all my friends across the globe, thank you.

To Liam O'Shea and Susan Murphy in Clare FM, thank you for the opportunity and experience in the media and also to my friend Mike McCartney for his support and opportunity on radio. A big thank you to journalist Tara King for writing and compiling this book.

To all from the GAA for their support and opportunities, especially to a great friend and legend Davy Fitzgerald and the late Fr Michael McNamara PP, former chairman of Clare County Board, who gave me great encouragement in times of need. To all our therapists past and present a big thank you for your hard work. Thank you to Bernadette Bohan for her contribution on juicing and nutrition in the chapter, Your Own Personal Plan: Diet and Medication.

Most importantly, to all the people of Ireland for putting your trust in us over the years, especially to those who have had the courage to tell their stories in the media and in this book. Continued success of your health and happiness and may God bless you and your families always – your courage will inspire others.

To Sharon O'Loughlan and Carina Rosengrave for all their hard work, help and support. To Patrick Bourke Menswear and Jean McCabe of Willow Boutique, Ennis for providing clothing for various photoshoots and model Martina Costello for her professional guidance and support.

To Michael Flatley a big thank you for having the courage to tell the world of the benefits of my work. Your generosity and kindness know no bounds and many, many people are free from suffering as a result. May God continue to bless and protect you and your wonderful family. I wrote this book because of the encouragement and opportunity you presented me with.

Foreword

Yes. Energy is everything and everything is energy. In order to understand how the human body works, we must first understand the flow of energy. When energy flows freely life seems great, when it is blocked everything seems to go wrong – it's really that simple. A few years ago I was struck down with a mystery illness; all the king's horses and all the king's men couldn't diagnose the problem, how could they ever prescribe a cure? Enter Michael O'Doherty.

It is difficult to explain adequately how energy works, I just know it works. Michael O'Doherty visited me at Castlehyde during my illness and he was instantly able to restart the flow of energy through my body. I immediately began to feel better. Within days I felt back to my normal self.

Energy healing transfers positive energy from the healer to the patient, removing any and all energy blocks so that the body can heal itself, which it is perfectly capable of doing. It is 100 per cent natural and it works! Michael O'Doherty is the consummate purveyor of positive energy. His mere presence brings positive energy into a room. Well educated, well read and well versed, there are few people I know that are more willing or able to educate and enlighten us on this powerful subject. He has helped thousands and thousands of people around the world.

Yes, when I was asked to write the foreword for this book, I immediately agreed without hesitation. Yes, I believe in positive energy; if you believe in yourself and are willing to work hard to follow your dreams, then nothing is impossible. Yes, I believe in the power of healing energy, I believe in the universe and all that is good. Yes, I believe in Michael O'Doherty.

Michael Flatley

Preface

Both Michael O'Doherty and I have discussed on many occasions our life experiences in relation to the healing work we have done over the last twenty years and the effects it has had on our lives and the lives of many thousands of people. Our discussions of late are coloured by a powerful ingredient – experience. We have noted the changes within ourselves and in our environment igniting an excitement and optimism about our future.

We believe that there is an enormous amount of hidden potential within each of us to face any challenge that life throws at us and that it is through overcoming these challenges that we learn and evolve. We believe that as human beings we are constantly trying to understand ourselves, our inner world, our impulses, desires, emotions and feelings, the inner world of soul and spirit, our conscious minds and our subconscious influences. Contrast this with the outside world of business, finance, career and the constant need to find the right job and environment to support self and family. There is no doubt that the world we live in today is a precarious place where sudden changes and economic structures can be beneficial or detrimental to our financial and social status.

Michael and I believe that in the midst of all the chaos, where economic systems are being redefined and traditional religious institutions and belief systems are being challenged, paradoxically there is also an opportunity for growth. We believe that rediscovering the feminine energy as distinct from female is the way forward for people to rediscover their true power and potential. The feminine or goddess energy is that which is spiritual, communicates with Mother Earth, plants, animals and the spirit of nature through energy in the web that unites all. Most importantly, this involves cyclical thinking as distinct from linear thinking. Linear thinking is associated with ego, status, power, control and wealth as well as the left side of the brain, the male brain. With the economic crash, we feel at this moment people are beginning to redefine their value systems not based on wealth but on friendship, positive human interaction and looking inward for a sense of spirituality. This is evident today by the amount of people taking part in meditation practices and availing of complementary healing therapies such as Plexus bio-energy.

People are realising that opening up to their psychic potential can give meaning to their lives and help them consciously realise that they can find inner peace and love by turning inward and rediscovering the feminine, which is associated with the right brain hemisphere. A rediscovery of the feminine element is a realisation that we are connected to everything and everyone and that every positive and negative thought can make a difference to our future and to our physical mental, emotional and spiritual well-being. We realise that at every conscious moment we are connected to the past through our ancestral bloodline and genetics. We have seen tremendous healing in people when we help them offload the negative ancestral debris that they have carried with them into this world through leading-edge techniques that we have developed.

We are also connected and influence our future through our present state of mind, our thoughts and attitudes. Cosmologists are telling us that we are multidimensional beings existing in several realities simultaneously and there is an inexhaustible source of energy at the very core of our reality. Through the discovery of the feminine energy, we can tap into this energy. We have seen people recover from being very ill to healthy, happier people in a very short period of time through our Plexus bio-energy treatments. We realise that the techniques developed to manipulate the energy are very powerful tools in the hands of a therapist and that healing people should be followed by education and training, thereby empowering people to take control of their own lives.

We believe that the disciplines of medicine, psychiatry and psychology have a part to play in helping people to evolve. However, it is unfortunate that the practitioners of these disciplines have not experienced the transforming power of bio-energy therapy and vibrational medicine and the holistic way it engages the individual. Unfortunately, there is still a lot of religious and scientific taboo that makes it difficult for these institutions to break away from their rigid belief systems and structures; however, we feel that this is beginning to change and likely to be more so in the future.

We leave an open door for scientists and doctors to look closely at our non-chemical drug-free approach to healing and the benefits this has on people's health and the effects it may have on society. Our ethos is to share knowledge and experience for the benefit of all. The time has come for a shift of consciousness that will bring about a new understanding of who we are, how we function, and how we can resonate at a level where sickness can be a thing of the past.

Tom Griffin
Co-founder of Plexus

Testimony of Michael Flatley

In late 2006, dancer and choreographer Michael Flatley was struck with a severe unknown virus. It left his body exhausted and weak resulting in what is termed post-viral fatigue syndrome. Where once Michael had been gracing the world stage with boundless energy, he now had symptoms ranging from severe lethargy to muscular pain and an inability to focus.

'I was tired, I had no energy, I couldn't work and I had to cancel a tour,' Michael recalls. 'I was beginning to think I would never be back to full health, then I met Michael O'Doherty and things began to change for the better. '

After spending almost a year trying to regain his health, Michael was introduced to Michael O'Doherty of the Plexus Bio-Energy Clinic. Following the initial meeting where he learned about Michael's illness, Michael O'Doherty commenced a series of treatments. Remarkably, after the first session, the effects became apparent immediately. Michael took his first long walk in over a year and his mind became clear. Here he recalls his own treatment process and offers advice to those who may be suffering in some way and looking for an answer.

'I was tired, I had no energy, I couldn't work and I had to cancel a tour,' Michael recalls. 'I was beginning to think I would never be back to full health, then I met Michael O'Doherty and things began to change for the better.

'I have always had faith in alternative treatments and during the course of my illness, I had tried conventional medicine and also several alternative methods of treatment but none of them relieved my suffering long term.

'Following my first meeting with Michael I immediately felt better. After an hour of energy-healing treatment, I felt revived and was able to go for a long walk – something I had been unable to do for months. My energy had shifted and was now beginning to flow again. In the long term, it has made a huge improvement to my overall well-being. No matter what your problems are, they can be cured if your energy is cleared and moving again.

'The Chinese are 5,000 years ahead of the rest of the world with regard to their medical practices and yet their medicine is based on chi and the parts of the body that you can't actually see. If your energy is moving, then it's going to help everything.

'It is clear that Michael O'Doherty is extremely well versed in energy healing and has done extensive research in the field. The results of his treatments on thousands of clients are proof that his methods can cure almost any illness and vastly improve the quality of people's lives. When you are positive, great things will happen, and Michael O'Doherty is one of the most positive and hard-working people I've met.'

When you are positive, great things will happen, and Michael O'Doherty is one of the most positive and hard-working people I've met.

Michael Flatley

✵ 1 ✵

My Journey

As I stroll down the street in Ennis, County Clare, I observe the faces of people as they walk past, expressing uncertainty. The tabloids festoon the newspaper stands lining the shop windows, each one bearing the same story as the next. Alongside threats of economic doom and gloom and photographs of stockbrokers burying their heads in their hands, the lead story taking up most front pages concerns the suicide of a property developer. Also, words from the Government telling us of the need for serious cuts in spending and banks under serious pressure are leading to huge depression of our society and a bleak future.

These kinds of headlines are pushed in our faces every day and at times we worry that such problems will somehow beat a destructive path into our own lives. However, what we do not realise is that by absorbing such information and allowing it to cause an element of fear and anxiety within our psyche, we are providing negativity with the perfect opportunity to breed disease in our system. Always remember, negative thoughts lead to negative feelings, which in turn can lead to illness and disease. Your life has the potential to be phenomenal and healthy, so why spend it in the waiting room of your local GP, or worse, in a crowded A&E.

Any archery enthusiast will tell you that the essence of flight archery is to see how far you can shoot the arrow. The one thing I would like you to do from this day forward is to envision yourself as the flight archer and see how far you can go in life. More importantly, however, I would like you to promise yourself that you will try to go as far as you possibly can. I would like you to stop using excuses for reasons not to do things, but rather instead to try to make excuses to do things and to change your life for the better. In order to be able to achieve this goal, you will require both your physical, mental, emotional and spiritual health to be in peak condition. This book will not only show you just how you can achieve that but it will

People are always blaming their circumstances for what they are. I don't believe in circumstances. The people who get on in this world are the people who get up and look for the circumstances they want, and if they can't find them, make them.

George Bernard Shaw

also furnish you with everything you need to know in order to eliminate the possibility of ever having to experience illness in your life again.

First things first, however. If I am going to be able to help you in your life, I will need to gain your trust. For this to happen, you will need to know something about me and how I became involved in the field of healing.

Early years

I was brought up in West Clare in the mid-1960s. It was back in that difficult period in Ireland when times really were 'the hard times' and when niceties were rare if not non-existent. Having been born into a family of ten, let me tell you with full assurance that resilience was bred well into my bones by the time I could walk! Maybe my optimism was also formed somewhere deep in those early years too. Because when I look back on my life, I cannot help but remember my mother Phyllis recalling the night that I, as a newborn, was admitted to hospital and nearly died from severe gastric problems.

Prior to this, I had suffered a lot with digestive problems, colic symptoms and huge gastric upsets. However, on one particular night, the problem worsened, sending shards of pain throughout my tiny body. I believe at the time I was suffering from, along with everything else, a twisted gut. Mum and Dad can still remember vividly the moment they were both told that my chances of survival were highly unlikely due to the nature of the gastric problems I was experiencing. It was exceptionally difficult for my mother to hear this, as her other son had died not long before I was born. Summoning all their strength in the hospital that night, she and my father Michael willed me to live and maintained that core of optimism from there on in. After about two years, my body had fully recovered from the turmoil, although this was certainly no quiet recovery! Any time my mother recalls that period in my life, she jokes that she could never shut me up because I was always crying! I have often seen her smile and say, 'For two years, I walked the floor with that fella!' While fortunately she and I can now look back on that time with teasing banter, to this day, I firmly believe it was precisely that wonderful care, love, positivity and effort from my parents that led to my recovery in the end.

Following the drama of those early years, my life played itself out in the small coastal Clare village of Doonbeg. Like everyone else in the area, I attended Doonbeg National School before going on to Kilkee Vocational School. Even though education was treated as an important fixture in a young person's life, I remember at the time there was always that need to get out and work. My father, like his father before him, had a tailoring business in Kilkee, and constantly emphasised the importance of a good work ethic. From an early age he instilled in us the motivation to achieve our ambitions. The one thing he never wanted to see was one of us out of work, simply because he always felt there were so many opportunities out there for us and such great things that hard work would help us achieve.

With this in mind, I took my first step towards the working world right after I had completed my Intermediate Certificate exam. At the time, I decided I wanted to work in the hotel industry. Not only was it an area in which I had developed a huge interest but, from a career point of view, it was the main attraction in Ireland at the time. Our burgeoning tourism industry was right on the cusp of really kicking off. Many people were beginning to get involved in this particular field, so to give myself a firm footing in the sector, I enrolled in a hotel business course in the Regional Technical College Galway, the present-day Galway IT. Once I had completed the course, I successfully sourced work in a couple of hotels in Clare. Eventually, however, I moved to Malahide in Dublin where I worked in the Grand Hotel. It was there that I became friends with a man named Pat Tierney who one day shared with me his ambitions to join the Air Corps. By that point, my taste of the hotel business had left me feeling that maybe it was not my forte. So, inspired by the ambitions of my friend, not to mention armed with my own ambitions to progress in the working world, I too looked into the possibility of joining the Air Corps. Shortly afterwards, I signed up.

I suppose it seems like I suddenly jumped from one extreme to the other by going from hotel work to military work, but whenever I look back on my earlier years I can clearly see just how everything really did happen for a reason, and why, if you let it, fate's hands will take wonderful care of you. Perhaps it was my coastal upbringing, but I always harboured a huge interest in air sea rescue. Joining the Air Corps also served to fuel my aspirations of becoming a pilot one day. I have often thought about what I would be doing today had I not pursued a career in healing and, to be honest, I always like to think I would have progressed within the Air Corps. Maybe it's the action man inside every boy that is coming out in me here, but I loved the whole military scene, and everything I learned during that period I carried with me throughout my life. In this regard, I suppose the Air Corps is the one part of my life that I look back upon with an element of regret, as it would have been fantastic if I could have stayed there. Instead, I remained in the job for about a year after joining. Although I had absolutely loved every minute of working with them, it struck me that there was more money to be made from a job in the Irish Prison Service.

One of my sisters was working for the Prison Service at the time and, as far as financially secure jobs went, the Prison Service was a great option. My first base in the Prison Service was Shanganagh Castle in Shankill, Co Dublin. Following this, I was stationed in St Patrick's Institution, part of Mountjoy Prison, after which I then took up a post in Limerick Prison. In 1984, however, I found myself working in Cork Prison and during that same year, a man, hailing from Claremorris, County Mayo, by the name of Tom Griffin joined. Funnily enough, the first person he met upon his arrival was me. I had been asked to show him around that day but little did I realise at the time how our meeting would prove hugely influential in relation to the work we would be doing twenty years on. In fact, the old adage 'what's for you won't pass you' always springs to mind when I think of how our paths crossed. Tom had been training in a seminary as a priest before going on to join the army, which he then left to join the Prison Service. Apart from the priesthood aspect, our backgrounds were actually quite similar.

Working in the Prison Service was fine but I only ever saw it as a temporary job; I never envisioned it as the way I would continue my life. My role as a prison officer was, I felt, a soul-destroying one. I actually felt at the time that the only difference between the officers and the prisoners was that we were able to go home at the end of the day. The job just did not provide for creativity. Either you were turning a key or you were walking up and down the landing; some days you would be in court, but all in all it was more of an observation than a job. Admittedly, it was a difficult profession at times but you always found a way to adapt to the environment you were working in. People simply got on with it and many made a good living from it, but I had just felt it was not for me. Perhaps my problem was that I saw the prison system as a place of rehabilitation; I always felt there was a need to rehabilitate and communicate with the prisoners so that when they had served their time, there was less chance of them reoffending. However, the Prison Service in Ireland does not rehabilitate, it exacerbates people's problems, and this frustrated me greatly.

At twenty years of age, I was probably one of the youngest people ever to join the Irish Prison Service. There came a point, however, when I could not help but think is was really the life for me. In one sense, I am glad I grasped the opportunity to leave the service when I did. At the same time, though, I do firmly believe it was fate that guided me there in the first place, because otherwise I would not have met Tom. For that reason, I will always be thankful for the part it played in my life.

Tom and I both shared an interest in martial arts and both of us became involved in kickboxing. Prior to doing so, I had trained in different styles of martial arts and I always found that it helped me to focus my mind and strengthen my belief in myself. The great thing about martial arts is that it exposes you to an understanding that there are energies and forces you can tap into. It was never about emphasising your outer physical power; it was always about utilising your internal power. I had developed this habit, whereby I would silently reassure myself that although the injuries would hurt while I was training in kickboxing, I would be able to overcome them, remain focused and go on to achieve whatever I had set my sights on. In this sense, I always had a huge interest in how the mind functioned in relation to sport, but I never envisaged in any way that it would result in something I could take a step further and establish as a healing career.

Believe it or not, the Gaelic Athletic Association (GAA) played a vital role in my internal development as a healer. Growing up in Doonbeg, I remember the people who trained us always forced us to believe that we could achieve certain things that perhaps we would have otherwise assumed were out of our reach. Bear in mind, Doonbeg GAA Club was a successful club and if you wanted to be a successful player you had to abide by high standards. As a result, there was always that vein of thought seeking to find ways to push yourself that extra bit further. I suppose I carried that momentum forward into marital arts and developed it from there.

When our initial kickboxing programme no longer fed our inquisitive nature regarding the workings of martial arts, Tom and I decided to study a different form of kickboxing called Mugendo. Developed by George Canning in Dublin, Mugendo was a full contact martial art that we found wonderful for physical training and development. Around 1988, Tom and I became aware through George of a gentleman called Zdenko Domančić who had developed a system in the former Yugoslavia known as bio-energy therapy. We learned more about

Zdenko's revolutionary work through one of our martial arts teachers, Peter Madjaic, who had been working with Zdenko at the time. Another mentor of ours, George Canning, had also visited Zdenko in Yugoslavia to witness the workings of this new bio-energy therapy. Upon his return home, he furnished us with the details of this remarkably powerful energy work. It was at this point that Tom and I decided to accept an invitation to travel to Zdenko's clinic in Croatia, then part of Yugoslavia, to observe this bio-energy work for ourselves.

By this time, I had moved to Newcastle West in Limerick and, along with the healing work, I was also running my own school of martial arts. Fortunately, an opportunity had arisen some months earlier that allowed me to take some time off from the Prison Service to pursue my healing work and develop it as a career. I do not think I realised it at the time but this was possibly the most important stage of my life. When Tom and I saw for ourselves the effect this therapy was having on people's health in Yugoslavia, we could not but accept that what we were witnessing was a very real breakthrough in alternative medicine. There were literally thousands of people queuing up on an island off Zadar waiting to be treated, and the results were astonishing.

Zdenko Domančić's inscription

We could see for ourselves the difference this therapy was having on people's lives, and so, after spending a week at the clinic, we asked Zdenko what we needed to do upon our return to Ireland in order to share his therapy work with the people there. I will never forget that moment when he took out the book that he had written and, on the inside page, adorned it with the message: 'This is my book and I am giving you the authority to translate it and to use it.' That was 1988 and we have never looked back.

The healing 'fella'

Upon our return, we set about treating friends of ours, never once thinking of it as a commercial business. Remember that we were not entrepreneurs, just martial arts enthusiasts. I was still living in Limerick and running my martial arts school, while Tom was working full time with the Prison Service. So for a short while, the bio-energy work was merely a sideline feature in our lives. Although we believed passionately in the huge benefits this therapy could bring to people's lives, we refused to rush the process, preferring instead to gauge the response of the people we treated. Once people started to notice an improvement in their health because of the treatment we had administered, I suppose word of mouth spread. As a result, great faith was placed in our abilities and this gave us the encouragement to continue the work.

Our reputation was given another push up the ladder when in the late 1980s an article about my healing work appeared on the front page of the *Limerick Leader* newspaper. Conducted by journalist Martin Burns, the interview had begun as a discussion about local GAA football, a sport which I had been heavily involved in all my life. It was only in the middle of our chat that talk emerged of my bio-energy work and the reaction it had received in the county since its introduction. Taking an interest in the subject, Martin arranged to have me photographed as I carried out my healing work. It was this very photograph that ended up on the front page of the *Limerick Leader* under the headline: 'Crowds flock for cures to local football hero.' Before I or any of the team could pick up a copy of the newspaper, however, we had a match against Limerick's Claughaun to play. Prior to the game, we were all busy psyching ourselves up in the dressing room at Claughaun pitch. As we went about our pre-match routine, I distinctly recall one of the opposition team walking in and asking 'which one of you lads is the healer on the front page of the newspaper?' I remember thinking at the time that there was just no way that my healing work would be front-page fodder so I elected to keep my head down and remain quiet. You have to remember I was in my twenties at the time and never in a million years would I have imagined that a simple demonstration of my work would make front-page news in the local paper. Following the match, I made my way to the newsagents. Sure enough, there I was on the front page.

The following morning, I was woken by the ringing of my apartment doorbell. At the time I was living above a pub in Newcastle West, which funnily enough was called the Crock of Gold, owned by Moss Dooley. Sticking my head around the door, I could see a queue of people, all of whom – a lady at the top of the queue informed me – were looking for the 'healing fella'. Obviously under the assumption that I was too young to be the 'healing fella', the lady in question went on to enquire if my father was about. I mustered some excuse about how I was not expecting my father back for about two weeks and slowly word began to filter through the queue that the healer would not be home for another fortnight.

I knew there and then that morning that I had to get out of that apartment, otherwise things would quickly have got out of control.

When we first began holding clinics in venues around the country, we always tried to distance ourselves from the religious aspect of the practice. We wanted people to see that they did not have to be religious in order to be treated. While we spoke openly about the spiritual side to the treatment, our main aim was to first help people understand exactly what it was we were showing them. We wanted to expel any possible preconceived notions that people may have had about our work. We wanted them to see that it was no form of witchcraft or hypnotism but rather a very simple method of working with the energy system, the results of which would see them back to their full health.

In 1989, a number of outspoken doctors unknowingly granted us a marvellous favour. While we were holding one of our clinics in Mayo, some doctors, obviously angered by the surge of people undertaking the treatment, decided to voice their annoyance on local radio. They claimed that there were healers in Knock – whom they didn't name – that were taking people off their medication. Of course, this was never the situation with us. In fact, the reality at the time was, and still is, that we would never even contemplate taking someone off their medication. People were simply getting better and, as a result, they were not returning to their doctors for more prescriptions. From this sprung the preconceived notion that we were taking people off their medication.

It did not take long for the claims of the doctors to make it to the printing press and sure enough the story quickly travelled to the pages of the *Evening Herald*. The next port of call for the debate was Pat Kenny's show on RTÉ Radio 1. I remember listening to the show one day and hearing Pat ask one of the doctors straight out: 'Isn't it really that you guys are just afraid that these healers will take business away from you?' All the controversy which the doctors' claims had ignited subsequently caught the attention of Bridget Ruane, a researcher from *The Late Late Show*. After tracking down Tom and I, she arranged to visit our clinic in the Bellmont Hotel in Knock, County Mayo to observe the work we were carrying out. Upon her return to Dublin, she pitched the idea to *The Late Late Show* team, whom, it transpired, were already aware of us. It seems the station had been receiving a huge number of calls from people all over the country either enquiring about the work we were doing or praising its results.

Michael with his wife Tina and Gay Byrne

In a way, we really could not understand what all the fuss was about at the time. As far as we were concerned, all we were doing was simply balancing the energy in people's bodies, which would then result in many of them benefiting from improved health. However, once we appeared on *The Late Late Show* in February 1990, it was like the floodgates opened and I can honestly say we were not prepared in any way for the response. Following the show, RTÉ received literally thousands of calls about us. I even remember Gay Byrne on his morning radio programme appealing to people to stop phoning RTÉ about us because the phone lines were already jammed and on the verge of burning out. In fact, he had to repeatedly tell them that we had left Dublin. I was since told that it was one of the biggest responses to a health issue on the show. Up until *The Late Late Show*, our position was one of just 'let's get this treatment out there and see how things go'; we already knew that the treatment worked. However, Gay Byrne was akin to God at the time and once he said it worked, then as far as the public were concerned, that was the most important thing of all. In my opinion, Gaybo is a legend and we truly owe him, Bridget Ruane and Bride and Paddy Walsh from Kiltimagh, County Mayo a great thank you.

In 1991, I finally finished my career with the Prison Service and Tom left shortly afterwards. At the time I was single, but Tom was not long married and had also just purchased a house in County Cork. The mortgage interest rate was at 16 per cent

Tom Griffin and his wife Tina

Michael and his wife Tina and dog Tiger

and, let me tell you, quitting your job at that time was a hugely courageous decision to make. Tom's wife Tina is also an excellent therapist. In actual fact, after *The Late Late Show* appearance, it was so busy that Tina was treating up to fifty people a day when she was eight months' pregnant with her second child, Andrew. An amazing woman! The year 1991 was also when I met my beautiful wife, Tina Downes, also a Doonbeg native, who had just finished her Leaving Certificate exams at the time.

She was employed by us for the summer with various duties such as assisting the patients when they arrived at the clinic for their appointments. About a year later, Tina began studying bio-energy and today is a full-time therapist. At the time I had never actually anticipated that something would develop in terms of a relationship. But through our working relationship we developed a great friendship and, as time went on, we started going out together. It just continued until eventually after fourteen years Tina got down on one knee and begged me to marry her! Ah no, only joking, it was a joint decision, but today we're still the best of friends as well as being co-workers and married with a dog named Tiger!

After 1991, many opportunities came our way. Our first book, *Bio-energy Healing: Therapy of the Future*, ghostwritten by the late journalist Derek Dunne, was a phenomenal success at the time of its release. In conjunction with media interviews and book publicity, we were also doing charity work for organisations like Goal and the Friends of the Children of Chernobyl. Chernobyl in particular was an eye-opener. I travelled to

Belarus in the company of a wonderful Clare man, Brian Mooney, and shortly after my arrival there, I set about treating a number of children. It is a place where you see real sickness; where the first thing you ask is how you can help ease their suffering. It does make you wonder what life is all about but you try to bring hope to people and do what you can to help them.

Michael and Brian Mooney with children in Chernobyl

In our efforts to introduce some of this hope into people's lives, Tom and I travelled extensively with our work, trying to make it available to as many people as possible. We went to both America and the UK where we held clinics for a number of months. You would find us in every sort of place, handing out leaflets that outlined and explained all about the treatment. In a way we had already established a base in these countries. The Irish communities already knew about us and we had also noticed that many people had been travelling from America and the UK to see us in our clinics in Ireland. In that respect, it was not unusual for us to be treating up to a few hundred people each day when we travelled abroad. They accepted us the same way the people in Ireland did. No one ever ridiculed us either, probably because they were aware of the amount of people we had brought back to health. Back in Ireland, my father often had to handle the many calls coming in and these would be mostly from people looking for appointments or asking which county we would be travelling to next with our clinic.

Following *The Late Late Show*, we worked in places like the Belmont Hotel in Knock, the Ark Tavern in Limerick, the River Room Motel in Newcastle West, Tubridy's Lounge Bar in Doonbeg, the Queen's Hotel in Ennis, but one of the main venues was the Lucan Spa Hotel in Dublin. We would have bio-energy therapists there tending to 500, perhaps even 600, people each day. Believe it or not, throughout all this madness, we still were not even charging people for the service! For the first four years after *The Late Late Show*, we simply did not charge. It was never about the money; it was purely about getting the work out there and proving to people what great things could be achieved if they adopted it into their lives. Instead, Tom and I worked on donations, simply because we had a small staff to look after, but we soldiered on and it balanced itself out. Ever since then, fortunately, things have improved considerably.

Back then both the national and local media were trying to source more information about us. People were even flying in from different parts of the world to see us. Such was the length of the queues for one of our clinics in Knock that the *Six O'Clock News* sent a reporter and camera crew to cover the story. There were often hundreds of people inside the hall, not to mention hundreds more trying to get in. Even though we were in our twenties and introducing people to a treatment that was entirely alien to them, we were never on the receiving end of any antagonism, primarily because *The Late Late Show* had exposed the benefits of our work. It had always been our position from day one to let the people decide for themselves; to let them decide whether or not it worked for them. However, while we were thrilled that the benefits of bio-energy therapy were now out in the public domain, there was a downside as I discovered.

Reaching breakpoint

There is a Sudanese proverb that says 'health is a crown worn by the well and seen only by those who are sick'. Indeed it is very true that we often do not fully appreciate our health until it is almost snatched from us. This is also one of the disadvantages to youth. Most people when young just do not appreciate their health in any way, primarily because they harbour a natural assumption that they are invincible.

This was certainly the case with Tom and I during those early years of our healing work. When you hold a clinic tending to 300–500 people on a daily basis, you're barely able to catch time for breakfast or lunch. You can rarely even leave the hotel without people pulling you in all directions. Even though we had our excellent bio-energy therapists working alongside us at the venues, all of whom were qualified to carry out the same work as ourselves, many people still only wanted to be seen by either myself or Tom because we were 'the two who had appeared on *The Late Late Show*!' In fact, another colleague of ours, Michael Enright, had also appeared on the show to demonstrate how the therapy worked.

We would find ourselves working from about 9.30am in the morning until around 11pm at night, sometimes even later. On top of all this, we were also trying to fulfil media commitments. Yes, the buzz, the hype, the demand, and the adrenaline fed our drive and kept us going, but I won't lie to you, it was incredibly difficult sometimes because we were not charging. We did not know if it was going to continue or if it was just a fad with people, and this was something that was always on our minds. After about three or four years of constant hard work, our own health began to suffer. Burnout was beginning to set in and we were all exhausted. The long car journeys to the different venues did not help either, particularly as the condition of the roads back then was so bad. We could be in Cork one night, then Kerry the next night, and then maybe up in Northern Ireland after that. As a result, there was a huge amount of wear and tear on the body not to mention a vast amount of stress. However, while we may have been experiencing our own turmoil at the time, we knew it was imperative that we kept our energy up and our focus in line. You have to remember that people were coming to us for help; they saw us as being the leading lights that would help them get better.

Unfortunately, something had to give way and for me this happened in Limerick following one bio-energy clinic. I remember walking off the stage in a hotel in Newcastle West and feeling as though there was not an ounce of energy left in my body. I can distinctly recall thinking at the time, 'what am I after doing to myself?' I immediately retired to bed and such was the strength of my exhaustion that I remained there for two full weeks. My body had simply given up. I was both stressed and burnt out. Nevertheless, these symptoms did not stem solely from the level of work we were carrying out; there were other contributing factors as well. Derek Dunne, the journalist who had ghostwritten our first book, had just passed away. This was a huge shock to the system because Derek was a great friend of mine and his passing had happened so suddenly. I see now that I was going through a serious grieving process as a result of Derek's death and in a way I had convinced myself that I was seriously ill.

I just felt at the time that there was no way I could have the symptoms I had without there being good reason for it, so I underwent the necessary check-ups and blood tests. Yet despite all the assessments, they still could not find anything wrong. Physically, mentally and emotionally I was weak; I was also depressed and suffering from anxiety. Although I was experiencing a huge wave of emotions at the time, I never once resorted to medication, nor did my doctor ever ask me to, as he was fully aware of where I stood on the issue. Then one Thursday night my wife Tina, along with one of our bio-energy therapists Michael O'Gara, came up to my room to encourage me out of my dejected state. They simply reminded me there was a lecture scheduled for the following day and that the people who had booked their places at the event would be expecting to hear me speak. For the first time throughout this whole ordeal, I threw my legs out of the bed and made a promise to be there.

I remember going into that lecture the following morning, taking my stool on the stage as I was barely able to stand, and looking directly at the 200 people sitting in front of me waiting to hear my inspirational words. That was the turning point that made me realise just how crucial it was for me to start taking my own advice and begin getting regular energy sessions and exercise. I needed to take more time for myself. That incident, while a low point, was one of the best things to ever happen to me, as it inspired me to change. I suppose after the first month, I began to feel good. After three months, I was able to get back to some normality, and after nine months I was able to look back and realise what I had learned. I opened up a private clinic in Ennis with the purpose of streamlining the numbers I was treating. This, as a result, helped me deal with the stress. I was also able to regain my focus but this was not something that happened overnight. It was a very gradual process, as I had to first overcome a culmination of stresses.

Only for the fact that Tom and I were young at the time, there was just no way that we would have survived the stress of the workload. However, while I do look upon that particular time in my life as being one of major strain, I still view the overall episode as being one of learning. I now make sure I have some energy work carried out on myself by one of my therapists. To maximise the potential of my health, I do not smoke, I watch my diet and I rarely drink. Most importantly of all, however, I make time for sufficient physical rest. Every day I thank God for my health, because apart from that one spell of exhaustion, I have since gone through life without any illness.

Training therapists

People thought it was great that Tom and I were in the newspapers and that everyone was talking about what we were doing. At the end of it all, however, we were still human, though admittedly for a while we probably saw ourselves as somewhat superhuman. To be honest when I look back at the particular part of my life, I can see now that Tom and I were holding ourselves up for the sake of our patients and everyone else. It was all at a huge cost to our health, but we worked through it, we overcame it, and from this we saw the need to provide a comprehensive training for those who wished to become therapists. The problem was that we could not go back to Yugoslavia during the 1990s because of the ongoing war. Essentially, we had no support from where we had initially acquired our own skills.

Now that we were out on our own, the first step towards establishing a training programme centred on trying to find the right vocabulary to explain what we were doing. We did not want to negatively impact upon the medical profession and we certainly did not want to offend the religious institutions. I do not know how but we succeeded in explaining our work without upsetting or offending anyone. Our first book, *Bio-energy Healing: Therapy of the Future*, was definitely a great additional help as it offered people an even greater understanding of our work. This in turn prepared them for what to expect upon their arrival at the clinic, whether for training or treatment. We wanted to make the training available to everyone around the country. In fact, we felt it was necessary, if only for the sake of our own sanity. There was a constant focus of energy on Tom and I because people saw us as the healers who were going to cure their problems. We knew it was time to accept that we simply could not be there for everyone; that we had to equip others with the required skills and instil in them knowledge that would help them enlighten the lives of others through their therapy work.

To do this, we compiled a list of techniques and put together a programme that clearly outlined to the trainee therapists the work involved. Following that, we went about the actual training process. We wanted to do more than just pass on what we had learned about bio-energy during this course of action. We wanted to educate the therapists in such a way that they could confront their own energies and emotions and maintain their energy levels. We wanted to emphasise the importance of the therapist's own health as well as that of the patient. As part of our research, I began to look at the Tao system, which deals with how the emotions are stored in the body. I realised that it could contribute greatly to a personal development programme, which we could then integrate into the course we were already providing.

Liam Fretwell

By this time, we had not explored the prospect of looking at diet, exercise and breathing techniques. Just working with the energy seemed to be sufficient enough. It was simply about changing the mindset of people and working from there. However, now that we were compiling our own programme, we wanted to develop the work even further, and thus these avenues were all explored. A Louth man by the name of Liam Fretwell had initially trained with us as a therapist but had since become very interested in the Eastern philosophy of Taoism. Like myself, Liam too had studied the Tao system with Mantak Chia, the person responsible for devising the system around working with the energies and emotional transformation.

As a result, we decided to introduce a personal development programme into the course. This was solely designed to help therapists maintain the high frequency and focus that was required from them to get in and do the work. It involved active meditative techniques, where the therapist is shown how to work with their internal organs, transform their emotions and move energy around the body. This would result in them transforming their own energy from stress into vitality.

Michael and Mantak Chia

Another pivotal factor in this programme is keeping the spine mobilised and the energy flowing through it. This part of the training programme was absolutely vital because, as therapists, we have to continue working even if we feel our own energy is drained. I think what saved Tom and I when we were dealing with the stress that hit us during those first four years was our training in the marital arts. Had we not acquired those disciplines, we would have experienced much greater problems. Martial arts gave us the stamina and energy we needed and made us much more accustomed to training hard.

In some way, I suppose we were the first people to give some credibility to the alternative medical field because we had used science to prove that our methods worked.

Bio-energy was a system that had already been scientifically evaluated. While our work was still in keeping with what Zdenko had created, as we progressed we began to develop our own input even more by researching the subject to a greater level. In developing our own programme, which we called Plexus, we worked with members of the medical profession and not once did we receive any hostility from them. While they knew we had always maintained that the answer did not lie in the drug system, they never channelled any enmity our way, because they too could see that people were getting better from the treatment we were administering. As always, we took every step to ensure that we were not detracting from what the medical and religious institutions were offering.

During the early 1990s, prior to establishing a clinic in Knock, Tom and I also held a meeting with Monsignor Greely and a number of other clergymen in the area to ensure that they were not offended by the work we were doing there. We were not out to cause controversy; we just wanted to help in some way to relieve disease and suffering. Of course, as a result of this, there was a huge weight of expectation on us from patients. The pressure was always there, primarily because there was a strong feeling of 'well you cured my friend, you have to cure me'. All we could do in this situation was explain to patients that we would be working with their energy in the same way that we had done with all the other patients. We simply tried to make it clear to people that it was all about a shift of the energy.

There were some miraculous results, and while we could not specifically explain how someone who was once confined to a wheelchair was now suddenly able to walk or why someone who had been diagnosed with terminal cancer now had the all-clear, we just knew that once we got the energy flowing, it would bring about a huge change. Patients often did not care how the treatment worked. They just wanted the treatment but, more importantly, they wanted the results. Gay Byrne had said it worked and for a lot of people that was proof enough. His word was the credibility that carried our work and we are forever indebted to him for that. When you think about it, the ripple effect from our appearance on his show was amazing. So many people recovered after coming to us, all because they heard what Gay Byrne had said.

Those were indeed strange but exciting times, but I think there was a deep sense that what we were doing was good. There was a positive culture there and, thankfully, I never harboured any regrets over choosing the road I did. As a result of the work I'm doing now, my perception of life has changed significantly in that I value it more. When you encounter so many people with illnesses, all looking for treatment, all seeking that sliver of hope, it makes you sit up and see what is going on in society. This is particularly true when medical science closes the door on a patient's hope for a cure, leaving them under the assumption that there are no other options, just 'miracles'. The only 'miracle' is that patients have not yet realised just how many other avenues are open to them. Why should the medical profession's lack of faith in your ability to recover kill your hope of living a good long healthy life? We always felt that there was something more powerful behind this treatment and that we were simply responding to a great need for it. There was a divine energy there and we always felt that if this were for us, then everything would work out. Looking back, twenty years on, I think we can safely say now that our trust really paid off.

I do believe that if I had not rectified my problems back in the early 1990s, I would no doubt have an even bigger crisis to cope with today. Throughout 2009, we have continuously been on the receiving end of national and international

media publicity, which was then followed by an enormous reaction from the public. This was primarily down to the treatment I administered to the dancing legend and choreographer Michael Flatley. Fortunately, I now have clinics and trained therapists to help me deal with the response and cope with the demand. We are currently providing training in Poland and are

Michael giving a seminar in Cork in 2009

in the process of taking it to Portugal, the USA and the UK because we feel the world needs what we have to offer. The key is to train people to do it themselves. Unlike before, however, I'm not rushing out to single-handedly heal the world and to be all things to all people. Thanks to my dark period, I now know what it is like to feel burned out, to be stressed, to feel depressed, and to feel back pain and anxiety. I know what it is like to be immersed in the dark night of the soul. I can identify with what my patients are going through.

Now that you have come to the end of the first chapter, you know everything there is to know about me. You know how I started off and how I came to be involved in bio-energy healing. You know that what Tom and I have created in Plexus Bio-Energy was no overnight success but twenty years of hard toil. As I look towards the next twenty years, I foresee a whole new level of awareness emerging.

People are beginning to understand now that things have to change. Individuals with certain illnesses are being told they cannot be cured, but we are seeing very different results in our clinics. Let me tell you about a lady by the name of Jennifer. She came to me with systemic lupus erythematosus, an autoimmune condition for which there is no medical cure. We treated her successfully and brought her back to full health. She even went on to train as a therapist herself. As fate would have it, Jennifer was good friends with Pat and Margaret Roche from Cork whose young son Wayne had committed suicide in 2003. Five years on, Margaret was still every bit as distraught as she had been on the day of the tragedy. It was as if the family was totally locked in that moment of shock, unable to emerge from the trauma. One evening Pat decided to phone me for help, desperate to seek a solution to his wife's grief. As you will read in chapter two, their moving story is one of great heartbreak and grief but also one of even greater inspiration and poignancy.

REMEMBER

Why should the medical profession's lack of faith in your ability to recover kill your hope of living a good long healthy life?

2

Grief

I can remember vividly the evening I first spoke with Pat Roche. The phone call was specifically about his wife Margaret, whom, he confided, had been feeling extremely down and depressed for some time. When I enquired as to the circumstances surrounding Margaret's depression, Pat explained how five years earlier they had encountered a hugely traumatic experience in relation to a member of their family. Their son Wayne had unfortunately chosen to take his own life on Valentine's Day 2003.

Here was this grief-stricken father on the phone trying his best to find some way to help his wife confront and overcome such a trauma. February 14th was firmly etched in Margaret's memory and, because of this, both her life and that of her family had completely frozen. I truly believe that it is virtually impossible to even imagine a parent's grief over the loss of a child. Just think, a young lad goes off to college with a wealth of prospects ahead of him. Next you hear he has ended his life and there is no explanation as to how or why he arrived at such a decision. Saying goodbye is the worst emotion for anyone to experience; however, when a parent is forced to say goodbye to their child at the graveside, it just does not bear thinking about. My own mother lost two children. Even though it was over forty-seven years ago, I still hear her talking about their anniversaries when they come up, while their births are spoken of as though they were only yesterday.

A huge emotional trauma can manifest itself in conditions such as headaches and depression but, in this instance, it also left the Roche family detached from society and permanently locked in the moment of when they heard what had happened to their son. We know now that the energy system of the body contains all the information of our experiences, and that it freezes in the moment of one of those experiences. In this particular case, the energy system of the Roche family had frozen in the split second of when the news of the tragedy was broken to them. It is often sometimes difficult to explain this process to people but that is actually what happens. The energy system freezes in the moment and all the emotion, the words, the environment, the noises – everything associated with that moment – stores itself within the energy system. When Margaret and Pat came to see me, they were still very much trapped. Every day they felt the same pain they had initially felt when they first heard the news. Even though time had moved some years forward, Margaret in particular was still living on a daily basis in that traumatic moment and the effect was taking a toll on her health.

When we receive a phone call from a person in grief over the suicide of a loved one, they are often just looking for answers, answers they cannot get because there is no one explanation as to why someone would take their own life. Personally, I believe it is just not good enough to say that the person who committed suicide was being selfish in their actions; there has to be a reason as to why that person decided to end their life. It is such a huge issue in this country today. When the other victims of suicide – those who are left behind – call to our clinic, they are at their wits' end. A glimmer of hope at finding a way out of their grief is almost like an unattainable dream. Fortunately, the reality is that there is a way out of this grief and it is most certainly not beyond reach.

To help an individual like Margaret, we begin by informing the patient of what happens when they experience this type of shock or trauma, how it affects the body and also where it is stored. We then begin to work on that energy system by using a series of specially devised hand techniques to scan the energy field. The techniques help us feel where the energy is blocked and we then go about releasing these blockages through re-establishing the flow of energy through the body. Based then on what we find, we carry out the treatment over four days going through the various protocols. We also equip patients with the necessary tools and techniques to help them independently cope with any emotional stresses that may suddenly occur. During the actual treatment process, we as therapists bring light to the situation by re-establishing the flow of energy in the patient. This is precisely what we did for Margaret when we began her treatment in the clinic.

As well as carrying out the necessary energy work, I spoke with Margaret and Pat in great depth, all the while being sensitive to their situation and very conscious of what they were feeling. This is a pivotal part of the whole healing process because, as a therapist, you try in some way to place yourself in your patient's situation. In this instance, Margaret and Pat were seeking help; they were not looking for a quick fix but rather a way to cope with their life situation. Their life had changed forever; that was no illusion, it was the grim reality. When they first came to the clinic, I as their therapist had to try and resonate with that initially, but I also had to try and find a way to explain to them why it is that their situation happened. Naturally, it is sometimes difficult to give an explanation for these experiences, particularly one so traumatic, but it is a very necessary part of the treatment. We have to help the patient try and overcome or confront the situation so that we can then ease the pain and suffering as much as possible.

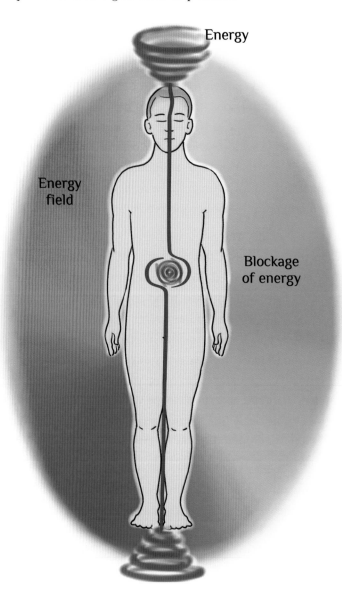

We began the treatment on Pat and Margaret the following Monday and continued it for an hour each day over four days. We normally equate emotional traumatic stress with the blockage of energy around the abdominal and chest area. It is almost like the heart area shuts down, and the whole body, along with the immune system, weakens. Tom and I had developed techniques to kick-start the energy system again and fortunately both Margaret and Pat responded very well to these techniques. They could feel the tingling sensations, the heat, the coolness, and the sensation of being pulled backwards and forwards. It was a positive reaction but, as well as reflecting just how blocked their energy was, it also served to show them that there was something outside the physical realm. This was hugely important because, as part of the therapy, I had to try to explain to them that death was not an end to anything; that their son had merely moved to another dimension. I believe we exist in a multidimensional reality, and I am very firmly of the belief that we have come from somewhere and are going somewhere; that this life is a journey from the day we are born to the day we die. As we go through life, we are all walking across that same bridge from birth to death, all heading to the same side. We have all heard of the bridge over troubled waters, well that is exactly what life is.

What I tried to convey to Margaret and Pat was that while death presented a physical separation and detachment from the person, when somebody is loved, they are never ever lost. This is a very powerful message that people, particularly those who may be grieving, should take on board. When someone dies, or departs this dimension, they simply move on to another dimension. I am certain of that. They go on to another place where there is total freedom of suffering and pain; where there is a great opportunity for them to help the family still remaining in this dimension. That is exactly what transpired from the Roche's situation.

When people react to the treatment and particularly when they feel it working, it helps them in some way to realise that maybe there is something else out there and that perhaps this is not the end. In this particular case, the treatment gave Margaret and Pat the realisation that they could still connect with Wayne even though they were separated from him.

A month after their treatment, Margaret and Pat were almost like two totally different people. They had resumed some degree of normality in their lives and appeared much happier and content. They were no longer frozen in the moment and so were able to move on. As their treatment progressed, we developed a wonderful relationship with them, and six weeks after their initial four-day treatment, we brought them back to the clinic to teach them some healing techniques that they could use on themselves. These same techniques are just some of the practices I will also be teaching you later on in the book. Fast forward a year and both Margaret and Pat were training as therapists themselves.

Testimony of Margaret and Pat Roche

How their son's suicide shattered their lives.

'We can see now how our health was affected by our grief over Wayne's death,' Margaret begins. 'It was all as a result of the tragedy and the emotional stress that came with it. You don't realise it when it's happening because you're just trying to take each day as it comes; you're trying to get on with life in the best way you can but it does affect you. Even though your body is moving forward, your mind is still stuck in that moment.'

'Looking back now, I would compare my sickness to a dimming light,' she adds. 'Before I got the treatment, I was at the point right before the dimming light quenches completely. It was like I went from one extreme to the other. I didn't have the energy to walk and I remember even going for a shower was an ordeal in itself. Afterwards, I'd just lie on the bed with the towel around me because I wouldn't have the energy to dry myself. Even my speech was affected; I could barely talk. I remember I didn't want anyone to talk to me because it was such an effort to get the words out. I often had tightness in my chest and sometimes this was accompanied by bad chest pain as well.

'I used to be so organised and on top of things but when I was sick, I didn't have the energy to do anything. Something as simple as making dinner could take me three hours. I'd go into town to do the grocery shopping but by the time I'd get in there I wouldn't have the energy to actually go into the shop. I was so sick but it was all because I wasn't dealing with the grief properly. I don't know what state I'd be in now had I not undergone the treatment when I did. In fact, I don't think I'd even be here today.'

Pat recounts their experience in dealing with the medical field as they went about trying to find a way to treat Margaret's debilitating illness.

'The doctors knew of Margaret's many symptoms but they still couldn't find anything wrong with her. They were doing test after test because they thought she might have something like cancer, MS or ME. In fact, the last specialist we saw gave her heart tablets and told her to take them anyway "just in case". It was all totally irrelevant. Nobody said "We don't know what's wrong with her". They just kept taking more money, putting her on more drugs and making arrangements to see us a few weeks later. Every trip to the doctor was around €60 or €70 and if you had blood tests, the cost was higher again. It just seemed to be all about the money.'

'We lost track of the number of hospitals and specialists we saw,' he adds. 'It was just a waiting game really. They would carry out many tests and then for about three weeks Margaret would be at home waiting for the results and worrying about what might show up. I remember we phoned to see if her results were in and were told to ring back at noon the following day because the doctor only took phone calls between 12 and 1pm. We phoned back and got the results but it was clear they weren't going to phone us with them any time soon. If we had waited another two weeks before phoning, the results would have been left sitting in an office while we were at home worrying about it. I know there's no point being bitter, but it just annoys us that the healthcare system is that way. It's just wrong.'

After the tests failed to shed any new light on Margaret's condition, Pat decided to seek the help of Plexus Bio-Energy after hearing about the treatment through a friend.

'I think the paranoia was beginning to set in because at one stage Margaret looked at me and asked, "Am I imagining it?",' Pat recalls. 'The medical profession couldn't help us so I rang Michael O'Doherty and told him about our situation and Margaret's symptoms. He knew straight away what was wrong with her and told me to bring her to Ennis to see him. He knew how sick Margaret was and so he felt that the sooner we could do the treatment the better.'

While the treatment would eventually prove successful for Margaret, her recovery was by no means immediate.

'After the first treatment session I remember I felt very sick,' she says. 'I told Michael about how I had felt after the treatment and he explained that it was natural to feel this way because it was as a result of the toxins leaving the body. It took about two or three sessions before I began to feel better. I could feel my energy slowly returning and I was beginning to do things again. My mood was also lifting. It didn't happen overnight though; every day was a step forward.'

Having witnessed firsthand the effects of Wayne's death on Margaret, Michael availed of the chance to offer some valuable advice to Pat before he too experienced the consequences of pent-up emotion.

As Pat recalls: 'When Margaret was on her second treatment session, I decided to undergo a course of treatment as well. I wasn't sick after it, but I could feel a strong dizziness in my head. I also felt extremely tired and I slept a lot. I do believe that if I hadn't spoken with Michael when I did, there would have been terrible illness coming my way. In fact, when we first met him, he pointed out to me that I was around a year or two years away from ending up as sick as Margaret. It's only when I had the treatment that I realised what he was saying.'

Although Pat and Margaret have long since given up the many 'what ifs' that can often plague people in such a situation, they admit that questions do still play on their minds over Wayne's death.

'Wayne was always a happy-go-lucky teenager,' explains Pat. 'He would sometimes worry about the future but once you talked to him he would feel reassured. One day while he was in college, we got a phone call to say he had taken an overdose and was in hospital. We later found out that Wayne had overdosed on paracetamol. You often hear of drugs killing people, but this was something Wayne had bought in the supermarket. He came through the ordeal but I remember he was very agitated because he didn't want to stay in hospital.

'It still doesn't make any sense, though. When the lads were younger, Wayne was the only one who could never take anti-travel sickness tablets whenever we were going on holiday. He hated swallowing tablets and yet here he was in hospital after having swallowed a number of paracetamol.

He was also the one who didn't like guns and hated being near them. Yet this is the same lad who would go on to take his own life with the same weapon.'

Pat goes on to recall a conversation he had with Wayne in the car on the way home from hospital following the overdose.

'When Wayne was discharged after his overdose, he seemed so happy in the car coming home,' Pat recalls. 'I remember him saying "Sorry Mam, sorry Dad, I don't know why I did that, it'll never happen again." We chatted with him and reassured him about things. We told him that he had nothing to worry about and that everything would be okay. During the time Wayne was in hospital following the overdose, Margaret and I went to speak with a consultant psychiatrist. He told us that we would have no more worries about our son and that the overdose was a one-off incident. He said it was a freak thing and that it would never happen again. You can't imagine how relieved we were to hear him say that. We really thought we would never have to go through something like that again. Just over two weeks later, however, Wayne was dead.'

Before news of the tragedy reached the Roche family, Margaret's instinct indicated something was wrong after she failed to hear from Wayne that day.

'I could see the yellow Garda jacket through the door and I just knew before I even answered it that they were going to tell me Wayne was dead,' Pat remembers. 'When the guard saw me, he said: "I'm sorry, Pat, it's not good." We were just absolutely distraught by the news. A lady who had been giving Wayne counselling actually came to the funeral and told me that she had spoken with Wayne the previous Monday. She then said she wanted to speak with me after the funeral. I don't know whether it was because of legal reasons or what, but we never heard back from her after that, so we still don't know what happened during those visits.'

Looking back on the week prior to her son's death, Margaret believes Wayne's way of saying goodbye was through spending time with each individual member of his family.

'The week before he died, Wayne spent a lot of time with each of us – myself, Pat, and his brothers John, Devon and Darren,' she explains. 'I remember him telling me all about college and what he had been doing *on the course. Looking back, he seemed very happy, but we have since learned that when a person has their suicide planned, that's when they are at their happiest.'*

Pat and Margaret now hope that by sharing their story they will inspire others who may be in a dark period of their life to seek out treatment and change their lives for the better.

Pat explains: 'I don't think people realise just how destructive grief can be because you always think you'd be able to handle it if something ever happened. After Wayne died, some people were a great support to us while others would say things like "You'll learn to let him go". You never learn to let someone go, nor would you ever want to. You learn to let them be. There's a big difference. Hopefully, this treatment will help more people do just that.'

The couple just recently became fully qualified bio-energy therapists. Speaking about their decision to learn the craft that changed their lives,

Pat adds: 'I suppose at first we just couldn't believe that people could be taught how to do this. We spoke to Michael about it and he explained that anyone can become a therapist once they are correctly taught the techniques. Personally, however, I think it's amazing that something this beneficial can actually be learned. It's even more amazing to think that no matter what age you are you can still benefit from it. My own mother, for example, is ninety-three years of age and she has gone to Michael for energy treatment.'

While the treatment has eased Pat and Margaret's grief, Wayne's spirit is still every bit as strong. Testament to this is the message from Wayne that was voiced by a psychic.

'One of our sons, Devon, went to see a psychic and what he was told was unbelievable,' Pat reveals. 'The psychic couldn't possibly have guessed the things he told Devon because he was so accurate. He said Wayne was sorry for what he did and that he hadn't realised what he was doing at the time. Devon told me that Wayne said he'd be there for us and that we were to stop crying for him because it was holding him back in the next life. He said Wayne also wanted Margaret to stop worrying about Christmas and that it would make him happy if we were to get on with our lives because we were holding him back by still grieving. We knew the psychic wasn't

making it up because he mentioned the names of people whom Margaret and I knew but whom Devon didn't know. It was so comforting and uplifting to hear what was said.'

'I think I have Wayne now more than I ever had him,' adds Margaret. 'He's always with me and watching over me. I don't have to go to his grave to talk to him or to feel near him because I just know he's always with me.'

Consequences of unresolved grief

In society, grief is often confronted with an air of 'Ah, get up and get on with it, you'll be fine'. Therein lies the problem. Some of the people we see coming into our clinics, ten or fifteen years after they have encountered some type of grief or trauma, have an illness or a disease that has come about as a result of their unresolved grief. More than likely, it went unresolved because the person chose to get up and get on with it, rather than deal with it properly at the time. If grief is not dealt with appropriately, it can subsequently manifest itself in conditions like chronic depression, rheumatoid arthritis, insomnia, back pain, breathing problems, and so on.

There are in fact a whole range of physiological symptoms that people can end up with as a result of unresolved emotion. As you know from the first chapter the Tao system deals with the issue of where the emotions are stored. According to this system, it is the organs that deal with the emotions and not the brain. In this case, the lungs deal with grief as this is where this particular emotion is stored. By this fact alone, your refusal to deal with your grief is another way of inviting into your system a variety of lung-related problems and breathing difficulties.

How we as therapists view grief is very simple. We see it as nothing more than a natural experience; something that we are all going to go through because it is inevitable that we are going to lose someone close to us. I personally became aware of the impact that grief can have on someone's life on the death of my father. For over three years I travelled through a deep grieving process, encountering all the experiences that accompany depression, anxiety, feeling down, not wanting to work, not wanting to go out, and feeling tired and lethargic. Due to the nature of work that I do, I was helping people to regain their full health, but yet my own father had just died from a stroke. As a result, this created a great conflict in my own thinking which certainly did not help my depressed state in any way at the time. However, when I look back on that period of my life, I know now it was a significant learning curve for me. It made me realise the huge need there was for energy work and grief counselling and how powerful they could be when combined.

The counsellor I dealt with, Ailish O'Byrne, was of enormous support in helping me overcome my grief through energy work, exercise and simply talking things through. I credit not one but all aspects of the therapy for having helped me deal adequately with my experience. It is imperative that people confront their grief or trauma in whatever way they can, otherwise their later years will be hampered with health problems. This is why I have absolutely no doubt in my mind that if Margaret and Pat Roche had not dealt with their grief when they did, disease and depression would have continued, with also the possibility of more serious illness in years to come.

You may not be aware of this, but our emotions are all the time affecting our organs. Every minute of every day, our organs are feeling the effects of whatever emotion we are allowing ourselves to experience. In the same way our lungs deal with our grief, our liver deals with our anger, our kidneys deal with our fear and anxiety, and our heart deals with love and hatred. When our organs experience these emotions, they send the signal to the brain, which then secretes neurohormones to try and cope with the situation. However, when the brain can no longer deal with the situation, there is a tendency within most people to automatically look for a substitute for the neurohormones, such as antidepressants or sleeping pills. Unfortunately, when using these 'substitutes' people can often find themselves falling into a cycle, and in some circumstances, an addiction develops.

In the case of Margaret Roche, we taught her not only how to connect with her emotions through the use of healing sounds but, more importantly, how to work with her emotions. In doing this, we taught her how to go about transforming the emotion she was feeling, so that instead of her popping an antidepressant when she was feeling down, she would simply sit back, carry out the breathing techniques as well as the active emotional–transformation techniques pertaining to the lungs where the grief was stored. In this particular situation, grief was the primary emotion but the secondary emotion was guilt, which is stored in the heart. In Margaret's case, the guilt came in the form of questions like 'Could we have seen this coming?' or 'Could we have done more?'

There is an immense need for education on emotions right now, particularly in our present climate where we are seeing an increase in the number of people being admitted to psychiatric hospitals. People need to know how to understand and manage their emotions: how they can be transformed, the negative effect they can have on the body, how they affect the brain, and how they manifest as disease like depression. In a later chapter, I will discuss this subject in greater detail as well as offering you techniques on how to work with the emotions.

Education

If we can educate people in how to transform their emotions, we will go a long way towards eliminating many problems in society. The breakthrough in medicine is going to come from people making decisions to change the simple things in their lives; to take the simple approach rather than dousing their organs in a variety of medications.

Those who make the simple lifestyle changes are the people who will see their bodies responding in a very positive way. In the Roche's case, we introduced these simple changes to their understanding of what was going on, to their perception of the situation, to working with the energy, and to teaching them the techniques they could use on themselves. This resulted in them feeling much healthier, much happier and now they have a remarkable drive and passion to introduce this treatment

If you could get up the courage to begin, you have the courage to succeed.

David Viscott

to those who may need help just like they once did. For Margaret and Pat, the therapy helped them deal with the guilt, grief, fear and anxiety. While it will never bring back their son, the fact that they are now helping other people benefit from this treatment has injected great life and positivity into an otherwise sad and tragic situation.

We are always worried about the next life but, to be honest, people really need to start learning how to live this life. The moment a person begins to awaken to this life is the moment they really start living. When I see what happens in my clinic, when I see those remarkable results from people who once had serious diseases, it is unexplainable. I cannot but believe with absolute certainty that there is something beyond this life. Our level of consciousness means we are incapable of resonating this. However, this is changing. Around 80 per cent of the people in our society believe in life after death. Quantum physics has taught us that we create what we believe in our mind, so once the mass consciousness believes in the afterlife, we create another dimension. We create an afterlife.

Sometimes people are angry with God, but really people are angry with the way life has turned out for them. We are brought up to believe that life should go in one particular way, but if that does not work out for us, we just seem to automatically blame God. Most of the time, people are also angry with themselves, but in fact it is in those very times that people turn more to the real God rather than the individual that exists through the belief of religion. I believe people are moving away from the religious perception of God and are realising that God is actually so much more. It is important that we tap into our own divinity within, because there is no external person hanging out in the sky with a magic wand who is going to sort out all our problems for us. I do not think people are angry with God, I think they are confused. They are told to accept the way things are, but it is not in our nature to simply accept the way things are. People have to be given ways to confront the situation because they feel it is just not good enough to be told that a situation was God's will. To say it is God's will is nothing but institution talk. The real overall message, however, remains the same, whether it comes from Christ, Allah, Krishna; they all wanted the one thing – love. With this in mind, I could never figure out why, if it's all about love, why would one have to suffer? However, it is through suffering that we gain a deeper realisation about what is going on in the human being.

Illness is an attempt to draw our awareness to a certain part of our being that we are ignoring. As I know only too well from my own dark periods, it is often these experiences that teach us those valuable lessons and force us to grow. The one big problem that people possess is not a lack of love but a lack of compassion. People do not know how to forgive others, or themselves for that matter. In fact, whenever I talk about self-forgiveness I always think of a quote from the great Buddha that goes: 'You yourself, as much as anybody in the entire universe, deserve your love and affection.' I believe forgiveness is the greatest power of all because in order to forgive, you have to love, and in order to love, you have to forgive. We need to have more compassion and forgiveness, and we need to learn to forgive ourselves the guilt that we may associate with an experience we have been through. I see it every day in my clinics, people full of guilt from past experiences. This in turn leaves them full of fear and anxiety for the future.

We are evolving spiritual beings. Over the past number of years there has been a spiritual famine because we attached ourselves to material things. However, as the economic circumstances of the present time continue to erode this material dependence, we gradually begin to find ourselves awakening from the illusion of affluence. We are slowly realising that we cannot base the future of human existence on economics, but rather on spirituality instead. After all, was it not science that discovered how the more we dissect and analyse, the more we find? What people need to realise is that they possess within their own bodies and minds the capability to achieve whatever they want to achieve. It is up to them to make the decision to commit to following through on their goal. It is up to them to make the decision to become the flight archer in their own lives.

I want you to realise that no matter what emotional state you are going through right now, or how it is affecting your life, that it all can be changed. However, you must be willing to change and make the effort to overcome your problems by taking an active approach, In my clinic, I teach you how to do this and we initiate the process by rebalancing the energy system of the body, defrosting the stored information in the energy system associated with the negative experience.

Do not waste your precious God-given life and wait for things to happen for you. Make it happen, take action now and embrace the opportunity to be happy and healthy. Take responsibility of your own health and when you make this decision, the universe will provide for you all that is necessary for you to recover. Antidepressants are not the answer; there is no chemical formula for love.

REMEMBER

'You yourself, as much as anybody in the entire universe,
deserve your love and affection.'

3

The Clinic

In the clinic, we treat people with all kinds of health problems from newborns to the elderly. Age does not play a factor in whether a patient is suitable for the treatment or not. The only requirement is that they must want to get better; they must want to improve their life. It is perfectly fine for people to be sceptical. They do not need to believe in the therapy because what we work on is real and undeniable.

When a patient comes to us for treatment, essentially the therapist will scan the energy field around the patient's body with a view to locating the energy blockages or imbalances. This is because if the flow of energy becomes imbalanced, stagnant or disturbed in any way, it automatically affects not just the physical body by disrupting its function and allowing disease to set in, but also the mental, spiritual and emotional aspects as well. The therapist scans the energy field by moving their hands around the body, but never at any point do they actually place their hands on the patient. While the therapist concentrates solely on the field around the body, the patient can sometimes feel different sensations. This scanning procedure re-establishes the flow of energy through the body again. Depending on what we find in this initial energy diagnosis, we apply a series of protocols. Some of these techniques are hands on. Once we re-establish the flow of energy, we know that the intelligence implicit in that flow can trigger the healing process as it alters the energetic frequency within each cell and allows the body to heal.

As well as the energy treatment, the therapist will also explain any immediate measures that need to be taken regarding diet, exercise, rest, attitude, etc. At the end of the four sessions, the patient is made aware of exactly what is required from them in order to regain the health that is rightfully theirs. Ongoing support will be provided by Plexus and if more treatment is needed then the necessary arrangements will be made. The treatment is carried out over four consecutive days in a private, relaxed environment using a background of specially chosen

Scanning the energy field techniques

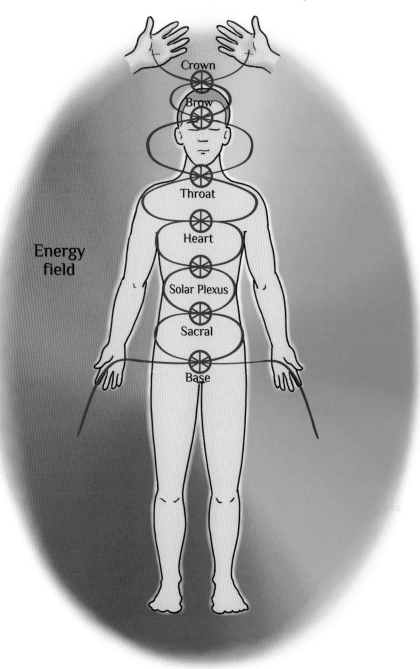

Crown

Brow

Throat

Heart

Solar Plexus

Sacral

Base

Energy field

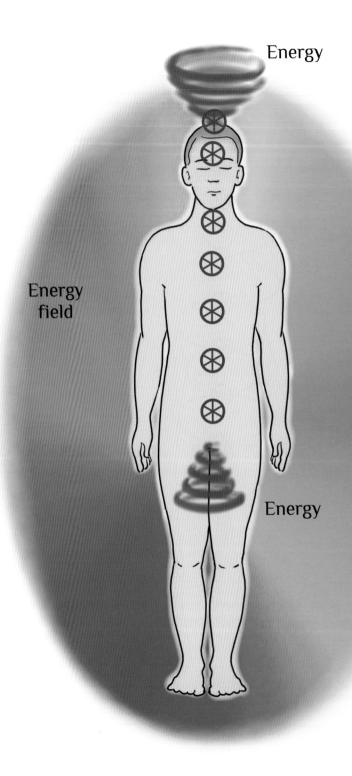

Energy

Energy
field

Energy

music that has been found to enhance the treatment. Most importantly, the Plexus system urges people to take back control and responsibility for their own life and health, which in turn leads to self-empowerment. We recommend at least two by four days of treatment for each patient.

Each person brings to this process a commitment of time and effort that truly reflects their own desire to be healthy. We basically reconnect the patient with the lifeforce in their own being. Absolutely everything is examined so that we can uncover the source of the problem that has caused the patient their ailment or disease. However, disease is not the only reason people seek treatment. It is often the case that a person will come to see us because they are simply looking to prevent disease from developing and also for stress-related symptoms like tiredness, digestive problems, etc. They often tell me how they have been to various doctors to find answers to their problems but all to no avail. Their body system basically is not working properly, but what the patient does not realise is that their body systems cannot possibly function right when their energy system is imbalanced.

I always liken the energy system to the foundations of a house. If those foundations are not right, then the building will incur a variety of problems and cracks before eventually collapsing. It is no different with your body. Perhaps the problem is that people do not fully understand their bodies as much as they should. They do not understand the importance, not to mention the long-term benefits, of confronting their fears, worries and all those other emotions they encounter at an energy level. We are not educated to understand this because we are told if we get sick, the doctor will sort it out. It is only when people are diagnosed with some illness that they awaken from that illusion. Institutions also need to simplify the way in which they explain things and the language they use when they are talking to people about their own bodies. By not doing so, they are distancing themselves from the people. In our clinics, our aim has always been to explain, as clearly as possible, how the body functions and how it recovers. We do not need to use difficult terms and convoluted language. We put it across in a way that everyone understands and what we find, as a result, is that people discover a greater strength. The key is language, and energy is a universal language.

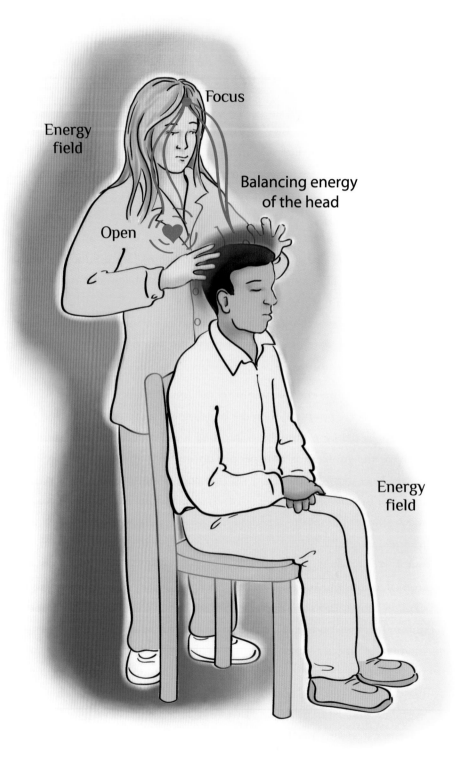

Naturally, there will always be those who are cynical about the work we carry out. Fortunately, however, we do not need to argue the authenticity of our treatments as the science is already there to support what we do. Prof Valerie Hunt of the University of California, Los Angeles (UCLA) has established that the primary connection to the world via our experiences is through our energy system. In her book *Infinite Mind*, she states that external electromagnetic energy penetrates the body through acupuncture points and flows through the meridians into the whole field:

> *We discovered that it also flows through the connective tissues. The connective tissue is the extensive structure which holds the body parts and cells together and composes bone, hair, nails, and skin by organizing cells into functional units. Without connective tissue, the body would be specialized protoplasm without unique shapes or functions. Connective tissue is also known to conduct electricity, although it is unknown what that energy is.*

She concluded that the electromagnetic environment is a milieu in which life and physiological happenings occur. Apparently, for all systems to be 'go', a rich electromagnetic field must be present. She observed that before the brain wave was activated and before stimuli altered the heart rate, blood pressure or breathing, the field had already responded. This in turn led her to postulate that a person's primary response in his world takes place first in the auric field (the energy field around a human being), not in the sensory nerves nor in the brain. Prof Hunt states that the implications of these findings are staggering. Effectively, the energy treatment of neuromuscular disturbances and degeneration such as cerebral palsy, multiple sclerosis and Lou Gehrig's disease should speed up the recovery process. Likewise, emotional disturbances, sensory confusion and learning disabilities could also improve. Why is this overlooked by medicine?

Many other contemporary scientists have added to the research, notably Prof Björn Nordenström and Dr Robert Becker. Prof Nordenström, a Swedish radiology specialist and a pioneer of needle biopsy now in common usage, spent two decades meticulously researching the bioelectrical fields of the body. His book, *Biologically Closed Electrical Circuits: Clinical, Experimental and Theoretical Evidence for an Additional Circulatory System*, has been ignored by conventional medicine, however. His thesis is that the body contains a complex electrical system that controls the activity of the internal organs and is the basis of health. In the application of his theories, he has treated tumours and other cancers successfully with specially devised electrical probes. Orthopaedic surgeon Dr Robert Becker also conducted research into the bioelectrical properties of the body and published his results in the book, *The Body Electric: Electromagnetism and the Foundation of Life*. His interest in the process of regeneration – hitherto unexplained by modern science – led him to conclude that the secret lies in the unifying bioelectrical properties of the body.

Start by doing what's necessary; then do what's possible; and suddenly you are doing the impossible.

Saint Francis of Assisi

The scientific fact of what quantum physics has established to date is that the human body is made up of energy. When that energy becomes imbalanced, the person becomes ill. It really is that simple. Unfortunately, people try to deal with their symptoms chemically through the use of various medications. Indeed while such drugs may alleviate the symptoms to a certain degree, they do not deal with the ultimate cause of the condition. It is essential for patients who come to our clinic to understand what is going on in their body; they give all their time to their illness and nothing to their health.

Over the past twenty years, we have been very fortunate to gain so much knowledge and experience to be able to deal with the problems that are out there impinging on people's lives – be they physical disorders or psychological troubles. However, despite the many advances that have taken place in the human body and mind, the one thing that has never, and will never change, is the energy system. When it all comes down to it, the crucial point is getting the energy flowing again. Once this is done, the intelligence implicit in that process is capable of correcting the body's systems. Following the treatment, we then educate the patient to continue and develop this good work through diet, meditation, relaxation or exercise, and sometimes the support of other services like counselling or psychotherapy.

Our clinic is very diverse, however, the outcome of the treatment does depend on the nature of the problem to a certain degree and the willingness of the patients to make the changes that are necessary. We deal with everything from sport injuries to babies with colic to cancer. While emotional stress and emotionally based problems all feature regularly amongst patients, back and knee pain is one of our most regular callers to the clinic. Unbelievably, huge amounts of people come to us with complaints of back pain, an area that medical professionals usually treat with anti-inflammatories, painkillers or surgery. In the vast majority of cases, however, these are not needed. When a patient presents with back pain or back problems in our clinic, we begin the treatment process as always by working with the energy. We then go about identifying the type of mechanical problem we are dealing with. Our experience shows us that there are three types of back pain: muscular, ligament and skeletal.

Once the pain type has been established, we then simply get the energy flowing in order to release the overloading of electrical activity on the muscle. This in turn helps the muscle and ligaments to relax as well as allowing the spine to realign itself. Sometimes the pain will warrant a programme of exercise or perhaps a deep tissue massage, but in some cases we need to look at the foot mechanics.

Poor foot mechanics

When the foot mechanics of the body are wrong, it creates a huge kinetic chain reaction often right up to the neck. If allowed to continue, this pressure on the neck area could eventually lead to conditions such as blood pressure, vertigo, hearing and eyesight problems due to the neurological implications in the neck area. There are, in fact, a whole range of physical and physiological symptoms that can develop just by your foot mechanics being wrong simply because of how it affects the spinal structure. People often look at their feet and remark how desperate or flat they look – both men and women. Women in particular, due to the nature of the shoes they wear, tend to suffer enormously from bunions. Even so, they often mistakenly assume that they inherited the condition from their mother. By wearing the wrong footwear, you are extending the ligaments in your foot, which can then lead to the joints collapsing and resulting in many problems eventually. If your foot is rolling excessively in one way or another and is flat, when your heel hits the ground as you walk the first point of contact after your heel is your big toe. Whatever weight you are is precisely the amount of pressure that comes down on your foot. This alone forces your big toe to veer to the right or left depending on your case, which in turn forces the joints to extend outwards. Once this has happened, you are left with painful bunions, which can eventually become arthritic. When non-surgical methods fail, doctors often refer patients to surgeons for treatment. Depending on the deformity, there are many types of surgery to treat bunions but one operation in particular involves a fusion of the joint. This surgery is not without risks. It can often lead to the restriction of both the joint and the toe, which can actually create more problems.

When the foot mechanics are wrong, whether the feet are rolling in or rolling out, the resulting chain of events will adopt the eventual process of ankle pain, back pain, knee pain and neck pain. This is simply how the body responds to an imbalance in the foot. We encounter many of these cases in the clinic, possibly 20 per cent every week and sometimes more. Despite this, it still never amazes me just how many problems can be traced back to poor foot mechanics alone. So ladies and gents choose your shoes wisely.

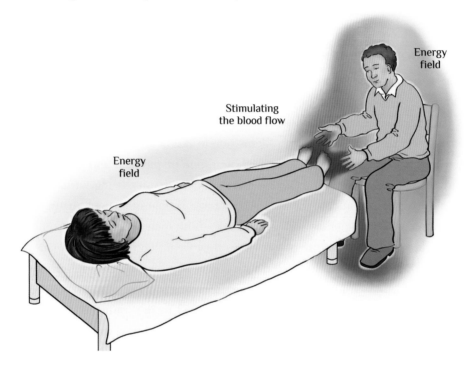

Energy field

Stimulating the blood flow

Energy field

Sickness – a big business

One of the big problems we see all the time in our clinics is the excessive reliance on prescription drugs. What we often find is that people who are taking a large number of drugs have been doing so for a number of years. They began by taking something like antidepressants but then as time went on, they ended up on sleeping pills. Because of those drugs, they may have experienced digestive problems that subsequently led to even more medication. All of this medication going into the system can lead to many other health problems, which ironically results in the patient having to take even more medication.

There are people who have come into our clinics with literally a bag of medication holding perhaps twelve different types of tablets. How is that any quality of life? The sad thing is many do not even realise that energy work could help them get rid of this baggage. The patient usually refers to the pills by colours rather than names. They will tell me they are taking the white one for one thing, a blue one for another thing, and a yellow one for something else. They do not know exactly what they are taking and, consequently, they are not aware of the side-effects of these drugs, which can vary greatly from minor discomfort to something far more detrimenta like sudden death. What I have often found is that people who are on such a large number of prescription drugs are no longer just suffering from the condition they were prescribed the medication for in the first place. They are instead suffering from the side-effects of the medication. That said, we do understand that no drug is without side-effects and that doctors do try to balance the benefits and the side-effects. However, I do think that doctors should regularly review the amount of medications their patients are taking over the years and decide which medications they no longer need.

It is also up to people themselves to take more responsibility. People need to become more informed about the possible side-effects of the drugs they are taking. In a way, some people are becoming much more informed nowadays. They are not happy to take whatever drug is given to them. But there is nothing more disheartening than to see a person come into the clinic suffering from a serious condition with a bagful of medication in their possession that is not resolving their problems in any way.

In my clinic I have seen patients who have been diagnosed with diabetes being placed on medications for blood pressure and cholesterol. While both their blood pressure and cholesterol may be normal, giving them such medication is still seen as a standard thing to do. Of course, doctors may be just trying to prevent the patient developing heart disease or stroke. Diabetics are already taking insulin for their condition, which if not controlled can very easily lead to renal failure, eyesight problems and circulatory problems. The cumulative effect of giving other medications along with insulin is not without risk. Statin medication, used to control cholesterol, essentially stops the liver from secreting fat into the blood. Though it is deemed relatively safe, it is not without side-effects either.

Statins in my opinion are being abused by medics who often fail to report side-effects. According to an article in the *Washington Post* on 28 August 2007, based on a study published in the journal *Drug Safety*, physicians often ignore or dismiss patient complaints about possible side-effects of statins. The study was led by Beatrice Golomb, associate professor of medicine at the University of California, San Diego. It surveyed 650 patients who resided in the US and who were mostly in their early sixties. The study found that most of the participants had complained to their physicians about muscle pain, memory loss, numbness in their hands and feet, or other possible side-effects of statins. The physicians attributed the symptoms to ageing, denied their link with statins or dismissed them altogether. In the article, Jerry Avorn, Harvard Medical School professor and author of *Powerful Medicines: The Benefits, Risks and Costs of Prescription Drugs*, said there was 'horrendous underreporting of side-effects', where as much as 90 to 99 per cent of serious side-effects are not reported by doctors to the Food and Drug Administration (FDA).

People need to ask themselves, are the multinational companies who are making these drugs really interested in our health and welfare? I do not believe they are. As far as I am concerned, they are interested in sickness because it is a big business and they want to push as many drugs as they can. Profit is their great motivator. We see the results of this in our clinics all the time.

If, when assessing a patient, we find that they are taking a lot of medication, we will carry out the energy treatment as per usual. We never advise patients to stop their medications but ultimately will advise them to return to their GP or consultant for a discussion about their medication. I had a situation around a year ago whereby a woman attending the clinic presented with various symptoms such as anxiety, pains and aches, and generally feeling unwell. Eventually, we found out that she was on statin medication. We sent her back to her GP who took her off her medication and shortly afterwards her symptoms went away.

There are people suffering from ailments that are often caused by the medication they are on for some other condition. It is time people question the testing that is carried out on these drugs and the possible implications of taking the drug on a long-term basis. Until such time when people begin taking responsibility for their own health, then we are going to continue to have more admissions to hospital and consequently more people choking our health service.

Personally, I do not believe we are being told the truth about medications. Certain prescribed drugs, despite being deemed safe for the market by the FDA, are sometimes later taken off the market following a number of patient deaths. Though the FDA has a reputation of being the most stringent drug agency in the world, inevitably there are situations where it could better protect the patient's interests and take more heed of side-effects. Some argue that the licensing of drugs is influenced by politics. For example, in the USA, Senator Patty Murray is a leading advocate for a strong, independent FDA and in particular has spoken out at the long delays at the FDA to get the Plan B contraceptive approved for over-the-counter sales. On the floor of the US Senate on 21 September 2005, she condemned the FDA for letting 'politics trump science in the way it approves medicines for the American consumer'. She added: 'Americans must have faith that when they walk into their local grocery store or pharmacy that the products they purchase are safe and effective and that their approval has been based on sound science – not political pressure or pandering to interest groups.'

An answer often given is that the benefits of the drug outweigh the risks. When it is your life at stake, it may not be so easy to say the benefits of the drug outweigh the risks. Frankly, however, nothing is worth risking your life over. Who benefits most I wonder, the patients or the multinationals?

In our clinic we are faced with people who are ill for many years and on lots of medication but once we begin to treat the cause of the problems, the results are often miraculous. However, we simply explain that it is all about getting the energy flowing and getting the patients focused on their health not their illness. The level of consciousness we bring to the treatment also plays a major role as we only focus on seeing the patient healthy. That is the reality with which we work. You do not have to suffer; as a human being you have the right to be healthy, so just go for it. What have you got to lose?

REMEMBER

If the flow of energy becomes imbalanced, stagnant or disturbed in any way, it automatically affects not just the physical body by disrupting its function and allowing disease to set in, but also the mental, spiritual and emotional aspects as well.

Testimony of Michael Lenihan

'The medical approach could only offer pain management and said I would never do what I used to do. However, Michael O'Doherty proved the medics wrong and cured my back problem.'

For farmer, Michael Lenihan, being able to walk is an accomplishment in itself. Considering what he has been through, it is not difficult to see why. For over a year, Michael endured harrowing agony from pains shooting through his back, and, at one stage, even standing straight was an impossible task. Doctors predicted a bleak future and could offer only pain management therapy when the painkilling injections proved ineffective. Fortunately, Michael opted to take matters into his own hands and actively sought out alternative avenues that he hoped would hold the solution to his problem. Here he looks back on what he went through at that time and recalls a routine that many are only too familiar with – various referrals and no answers.

'My problem first began in 1997,' Michael begins. 'I was driving a lot at the time and I remember experiencing a lot of stiffness in my lower back. It wasn't long, however, before it developed into a sharp pain. I went to a physiotherapist for a couple of months but I didn't find it helpful and in the end he actually advised me to go see a GP about the pain I was in.

'My GP sent me for X-rays and CT scans and afterwards I was referred to a Galway hospital. I had my first appointment there in January 2008 and afterwards they referred me to a consultant in Cork. After he sent back his report on my condition, the hospital in Galway called me back for an appointment but by this time I was in so much pain I couldn't even stand up straight or sit down comfortably. Lying in bed was also extremely painful and if I turned, I was in agony. Even getting in and out of bed was painful. There was no escaping it – my life was completely turned upside down.'

For Michael, the fear of experiencing the pain was equally as bad as the pain itself.

'If I made any sudden movements, I would get a searing pain throughout my lower back and hip area,' he explains. 'I had to watch everything I did; I was all the time dreading when the next pain would cut through me. I can't describe just how bad the pain was. It would really take your breath *away when you'd get a shot of it. Even the type of ground I walked on could result in a pain shooting through my back like an electric shock. I remember I was out walking in the field one day when I walked on some rough ground. I fell down immediately roaring in pain.'*

He continues: 'The doctors identified discs in my lower back that were causing the problem. They later called me back for four injections which were meant to relieve the pain, but to be honest I didn't feel any better after them. Surgery was an option but not an advisable one. The only thing the doctors in the hospital could offer me was pain management therapy. I was also told to take it easy, cut down on the amount of work I was doing and to be careful of what I was lifting. As I'm a farmer, that kind of advice was not what I wanted to hear.'

Frustratingly, the source of Michael's condition could not be pinpointed.

'The physiotherapist told me it could have been one thing or a hundred things that had caused what I was going through,' Michael recalls. 'I personally don't remember one particular incident that might have caused it. I just remember my back becoming very stiff over a period of time. I don't think the driving caused it but I'd say it contributed to the problem.

'Around March 2008, following my time in hospital, I visited a number of healers I had heard of through friends,' he adds. 'I travelled to various different healers in Galway, Laois, Carlow and Tipperary. They were all doing different things, but none of them seemed to do anything that gave me some relief from the pain. Sometime during the summer of 2008 I was talking to a friend about my condition and she started telling me about Michael O'Doherty the healer and how he had treated both her husband and herself. When you are at your wits' end with pain, you will travel anywhere to try anything that might relieve the agony somewhat, so I immediately contacted the Plexus Bio-Energy Clinic and made an appointment to see a bio-energy therapist that August.'

Much to Michael's shock and relief, a physical assessment carried out by Michael O'Doherty confirmed the problem was not with his back discs but his hip joint.

He explains: 'I told Michael about my history and the pain I was in and he put me through a series of different movements. At the end of it, he told me I didn't have a serious problem in my back, but rather a mechanical problem with the joints in my hip. It seems that part of my hip joint was out. I remember Michael compared me to a car crash because my whole back had been dragged out of place. He then said he would be able to fix it but that it would take some time because the joint had been out of place for so long. That was a real turning point for me. It was a relief to actually hear Michael say that it wasn't my back that had been causing my problem because everyone else seemed to just conclude that the discs were out of place.'

Having gone from being unable to move without experiencing agonising pain to being able to resume his farm work, Michael himself is shocked by the change.

'I attended the clinic four days a week for three weeks,' he explains. 'As part of the treatment, Michael placed me on the ground and pulled up my right arm. I could actually feel the relief as he went about adjusting the joint. He had to do this on five or six different occasions as the joint wasn't staying in position. After a couple of weeks, I noticed my condition improving. The relief was unbelievable. I was given a programme of exercises to carry out at home which I followed religiously. They also advised me on which dietary supplements to take.

'I improved more and more with the treatment, but it was after Christmas when I really felt great. I still continue to go back for bio-energy massages once every five weeks as I find them very beneficial. I found that the massages really strengthened the area. When I first began the massages, I found it difficult to get up onto the bench, but now I can hop up onto it without any bother.'

Aside from relief of his pain, Michael took great comfort from the time and effort invested by the therapist.

'The medical profession told me to forget about doing the same things as before,' he adds. 'Michael O'Doherty, however, was the first person to tell me he could fix the problem. I can now walk, drive, work, everything I used to do before. Michael didn't just tell me he would fix it, he kept his word. The one thing I really liked about the treatment process was that you were given the time you required, which doesn't happen in a lot of places. If your treatment required a lot of time, then you weren't rushed, you were given the time. I can honestly say he literally gave me my life back.'

4

Disease: A Natural Reaction to an Unnatural State of Affairs

Our society exists in a consciousness of fear when it comes to illness. However, it is precisely this collective consciousness that feeds on fear and, as we already know, what we fear, we attract. When I look at people coming into my clinic they are usually very frightened of getting cancer, heart attacks, strokes, depression, and so on. They do not realise that what they are actually doing is creating the frequency on which disease begins and thrives.

The medical profession is continually telling people they should check different parts of their bodies for lumps, growths and other problems that might be a symptom of disease. However, I have no doubt that if a person keeps checking long enough he or she will most definitely find something. Quantum physics shows that our bodies are listening to everything that we are thinking. Our vision, thoughts and the way we perceive things have a direct effect on the body. This means it has a bearing on illness, though there can be other factors in the progression of illness such as genetics, the environment and lifestyle. In effect, the specific part of the body we are checking is actually creating what we are seeing. With this in mind, it is essential that we take control of our thoughts and our own reality to ensure that we are not now creating our own diseases.

One thing I simply cannot figure out is the advice constantly being churned out that women should regularly check their breasts for lumps. To be honest, I think this advice needs to be re-evaluated. My wife Tina and her friends used to talk about having regular breast checks for lumps and abnormalities until one day I told them straight out to stop. Naturally, my advice was met with some surprise and anger until I simply explained that if they kept checking for lumps, then that is exactly what they would eventually find. Just as we create our own reality, we also create our own problems. If you genuinely believe that you have something, and fear that something, then you will create it. This is not a Michael O'Doherty theory. It is a fact supported by science and quantum physics, whereby your thoughts have the capacity to affect your physiology and your emotions affect your DNA, as expressed by Gregg Braden in his lectures on the science of miracles. It is clearly established that if you keep checking long enough for a particular thing, then you will most certainly find it. This is because you will have created it in your life simply by looking for it; hence that is why I disagree with women checking their breasts *for* lumps. If you want to be safe and healthy then by all means check your breasts regularly, but do so for a different reason – tell yourself that you are only carrying out the check to make sure that your breasts are perfect. You are not looking for lumps but simply checking to ensure that everything is just right and that you will never find a lump. It is all about getting people to think differently.

Just imagine if we were to take the same energy that we invest in looking for a disease and instead channel it into preventing disease, we would be far healthier, not to mention much happier. This is why my sole aim for this chapter is to change your perception of disease and how you confront it. Remember your brain does not know the difference between a cancerous disease and a beautiful Mercedes car; it is just reacting to your perception of what it is. Most people who are seriously ill believe their condition is incurable, and if that is their way of perceiving the situation, then their condition will be exactly that – incurable. However, if they instead channel that same energy into believing they can overcome an ailment or a condition, then they have equipped themselves with the tools to allow them to achieve this. First people have to change their perception of the situation and not allow their future to be projected for them by the medical establishment.

I believe fear is one of the main reasons why people end up suffering from the same illness that struck other members of their family in the past. It is the fear of the disease that brings it on. People come into our clinic with something like depression or nervous tension and will often say 'sure my father used to have it, so I must have it now as well'. People have this notion that if a sickness or a condition was at some stage suffered by their parents, then they too will have it. Despite the genetics of a condition, the reality is that it does not have to be that way. If your family has a history of a particular condition, then by all means recognise there is a weakness. However, if you fear the condition in question, you will end up destabilising your immune system, thereby allowing the illness to eventually manifest itself. Remember energy follows thought and where your consciousness goes your energy flows.

On the other hand, if you keep your immune system strong and focus on the reality of health, disease will not be the outcome. In my family there is a history of strokes, hypertension, nervous tension and coronary problems. Nonetheless, instead of fearing that someday I may fall victim to one of these conditions, I instead recognise that these conditions are the 'weaknesses' in the bloodline and I take active steps to try and prevent these problems from occurring in my own life. I essentially maintain my good health by perceiving things in a different way. Despite the presence of serious conditions in my family's medical history, I steadfastly refuse to fear that they may affect my life at some stage because I know that by fearing them, I am creating them. You have the individual capability to overcome anything, even serious disease. Always remember that.

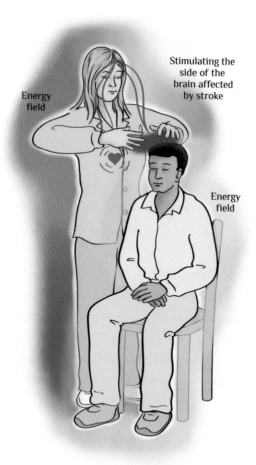

What is disease?

When we think of the word 'disease', we do not break it down and see it for what it really means – a dis-ease. Disease is merely an attempt to draw our attention to a part of our being that we are ignoring. It is simply a natural reaction to an unnatural state of affairs. When it comes to disease as we know it today, people tend to see the physical symptoms as being the actual disease itself; however, the reality is much different. The physical symptoms are in fact just the red lights flashing on the dashboard of our bodies; they are reflective of something going on much deeper. Disease is how nature works, and nature presents symptoms. The body's organs, tissues and joints are always indicating messages to us, be it through pain, stiffness, tiredness, etc. These symptoms are trying to connect us to an aspect of our being that we are ignoring. That aspect may be our emotions, our mental state, our attitude, our focus in life, or indeed our perception of life. Either way, it is a clear warning that change is needed. Instead of examining the underlying problem that is causing these symptoms, people by their nature prefer to opt for the quick fix. In the context of pain, tiredness, stiffness, etc., they take anti-inflammatories, painkillers, antidepressants and various other types of medications, and, yes, to a certain degree, their pain is eased somewhat. Nevertheless, the drugs are only effective enough to temporarily mask the real problem. Eventually, if the problem is not confronted and treated, it will simply remind you of its presence through another part of your body.

Pointless options

We have all heard and read stories about women with genes that leave them at risk of breast cancer. Some women with a high risk even undergo a preventive or prophylactic mastectomy, where they have surgery to remove one or both breasts in the absence of any cancer. They do this in the hope that it will prevent them from getting the disease that struck other females in their family. Now I ask you, what is the point of having a mastectomy? The problem does not come from, or begin in, the breast. The problem starts in the energy system and then simply *manifests* itself in the breast. What we have to try to realise is that cutting away a part of your body may not prevent disease. It is crazy to think that in this day and age women are made believe that they must have a part of their body cut off in order to stop a disease from occurring or spreading. Believe me, if it does not manifest in one part of the body, it will do so in another.

How to combat disease?

What we have to do in order to combat disease effectively is change our perception and understanding of what disease is. The simple definition for the word disease, as stated earlier, is that it is a natural reaction to an unnatural state of affairs. In most cases, the unnatural state of affairs refers to an imbalance in the body's energy system. Summing it up in one line may sound almost too straightforward to be true, but regardless of whether you believe or disbelieve, scientists – namely Prof Valerie Hunt and Prof Björn Nordenström – have established that the primary cause of disease begins at an energy level, as pointed out in an earlier chapter.

Many people have often visited our clinic after first having gone through various doctors, treatments, medications, physiotherapy, etc. What we will immediately do in such a situation is explain to the patient how their body has become ill (or dis-eased) through a breakdown that has occurred in their energy system for one reason or another. It is more the 'reason' we tend to address rather than the symptoms. While indeed there are genetic factors to be taken into consideration, for the vast majority of people, the genetic aspects only emerge because the immune system is weak. However, if the immune system is weak in the first place, it is often because of the emotional and mental stress that accompanies the fear a person has of contracting the disease suffered by other members of their family.

When a person goes through emotional stress, it creates a negative emotional frequency. Negative emotion creates its own frequency of energy, with different frequencies for sadness, loneliness, fear, anxiety, panic, worry, guilt, hatred and resentment. This is what the cause of illness truly is. Symptoms are there to prompt us to address the real cause of the problem. You will find that once you do so, your symptoms will disappear. We are often led to believe that we simply have to endure our symptomatic pains but, I assure you, your symptoms do not have to remain. There is a process, however. When people experience that change of frequency, sometimes it can require a huge amount of responsibility on the part of the patient because it demands significant, though necessary, sacrifices from them. They have to be willing to change their perception of their reality because if they do not, then they will continue to suffer. It is not sufficient to promise yourself that you will simply be more optimistic; your entire perception has to change, and this is much more difficult to achieve than you think.

When a person is diagnosed with a disease like cancer, their immediate reaction is to associate it with death. They will ask questions like 'How long have I left?' or 'How far has it spread?' Sometimes people do not even ask these questions after they have received their diagnosis because they simply resign themselves to the belief that this disease in their body will be the deciding factor of their fate. What they do not realise, however, is that their habit of associating death with cancer, or any other disease for that matter, is the type of thought that can be more damaging to their health than the disease itself. Granted there have been advances in science and some cancers are curable or can be well controlled, especially if detected early. But as long as the public consciousness believes that a condition such as cancer is incurable, then that is what the reality will be. It is time for medical institutions and individuals to stop giving false hope to people; it is time for medical science to stand up and express what we know to be medical fact, that the human being has the capability and the ability to literally overcome anything. If you are told you have a certain disease and that it is incurable, that only means it is 'medically' incurable.

You may not be aware that there are many other diseases that cannot be cured medically: for example, asthma, arthritis, Crohn's, diabetes, and many other conditions. They may not be as life-threatening as cancer and may be well controlled, but the fact remains there are no cures for them. The amount of drugs used for the treatment of these conditions are enormous and their side-effects can lead to a huge negative impact on the body. It is no wonder the big question now being asked is – what exactly is killing people? Is it the drugs or is it the disease? According to medical authority, the possible side-effects of the drug tamoxifen and other drugs given to breast cancer patients could lead to uterine cancer and even strokes. Tamoxifen is usually given to women whose breast cancer is sensitive to the hormone oestrogen, usually for five or more years after surgery. While the drug is well established in reducing the risk of recurrence, new research by Dr Christopher Li and colleagues in Seattle and published in *Cancer Research* in August 2009 suggests that the risk of getting a more aggressive cancer in the healthy breast is increased by more than four times. Out of 1,003 women with breast cancer in the study, 369 developed a second breast cancer. The second breast cancer was usually of a type not sensitive to eostrogen and harder to treat.

I know doctors will put forward the argument that it is a balance of benefits and side-effects, but there is simply no point in trying to cure one disease that could end up creating another, if not the same, disease a couple of years down the line. When people perceive a cancer as being incurable, what they are effectively telling their body is that it is now in possession of a particular condition that is never going to leave it, and because Joe Bloggs down the road died from it, then that is what is going to happen to them as well.

Once you create this as the reality for yourself, your brain is not going to know the difference because it is responding to your perception. As a result, it can produce certain neurohormones that can manifest themselves in destructive chemicals. Add this to the huge emotional stress and combine it with the negative side-effects of the treatment, be it chemotherapy or radiotherapy or whatever the case may be, and you are looking at a very bleak future. I cannot stress enough that just because medical science deems a condition to be incurable does not necessarily mean this is fact. Doctors often predict the outcome of a person's condition on the basis of all those who came before them with the same symptoms and test results. At present, there is not enough consideration of the individual and their ability to heal when it comes to the treatment of diseases such as cancer. I am not advocating that patients stop taking chemotherapy or medications recommended by their doctors. I very firmly believe that people can confront their health problems in ways using not just medicine but methods such as Plexus bio-energy therapy, emotional transformation techniques, etc. Drugs alone do not cure the disease; there is no magic drug and never will be. Drugs can treat the symptoms, but if you want to actually cure the cancer or whatever the disease may be, then you have to look at how you are functioning and from where the problem has stemmed.

If a person starts to take this on board, they will find themselves becoming more aware of how their body functions. Once this happens, it will lead to a shift in their consciousness, which will then result in a change in their perception and, subsequently, a change in their attitude. The overall result from this change in perception is an increased life expectancy. It will not be a quick process, however. Again, we have got to escape the notion of a magic cure. People who have serious diseases need to get away from this idea that someone is going to come up with a miracle fix. The cure exists only within their own body but it is not going to come into effect in the duration of a day, a week or a month. It is a continuous process that must be carried on throughout their life.

I strongly believe that a negative prognosis does not actually have to be negative. Unfortunately, the way in which diseases are confronted within our own medical system is sometimes negative, harmful even, and this has to be changed. Often people come to us with a bad experience, which they relate to us at our clinics. They tell us about their diagnosis and how it was delivered to them. It is often the case that they are just confronted and told: 'This is your condition, this is how you will be treated and this is how you long you have left to live.' Often people take a doctor's word as gospel and, without realising it, they end up ruling out every other option available to them. The patient totally focuses on what the medical perception of the condition is and in turn they feed the disease. We honestly do not know if it is the treatment or the disease that kills the patient; though I am sure the answer to that question will come eventually.

People need to realise that we have had such a huge increase in cancers and other diseases, and that there has to be a reason for this increase. The fact that medical science has not completely cured any of these problems suggests that we have to start exhausting other avenues. The real key for society is education. We need to give people the tools and techniques to help them confront their own emotions; to confront what really causes these diseases. If we can do this by starting in schools, by educating and motivating students, then it will not be long before we begin to witness a reduction in the number of serious diseases occurring.

These ailments do not develop over a week or a month; they can be formed during your time in your mother's womb or over ten to fifteen years of your life, perhaps even more.

Patient's reaction to energy field balancing

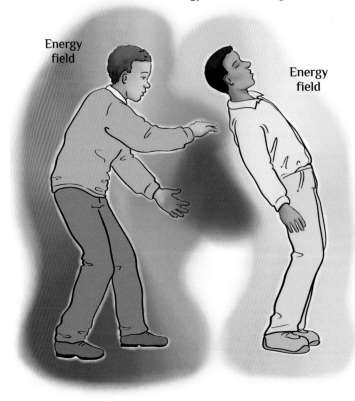

Energy field

Energy field

Chronic fatigue and burnout

When I look back over the many years of my career, the one thing that has greatly alarmed me is the increasing number of young people in their late teens and early twenties who are suffering from post-viral fatigue syndrome, also called myalgia encephalomyelitis (ME). Myalgia means muscle pain while encephalomyelitis is inflammation of the brain and spinal cord. If you were to ask a number of individuals if they knew of the condition ME, odds are they would know of it. However, if you asked them to actually detail the different aspects of the condition, it is unlikely they would be so informed. As I stressed in earlier chapters, we need to educate ourselves further and become far more aware of the risks to our energy system.

The condition ME has been described by the Irish ME Trust as 'a complex and debilitating physiological illness involving neurological and endocrine dysfunction as well as immune system deregulation, which is not improved by bed rest and can worsen with physical or mental exertion'. Other related symptoms of ME may sometimes include fever, sore throats, pain, irritability, poor concentration and sleep dysfunction. Sufferers usually pinpoint a viral infection as having been the start of their illness, although no one particular virus is present in all cases. According to the Trust, one theory is that the breakdown in the body's defence mechanism merely allows a viral infection to occur more easily. Unfortunately, however, I still believe there is a lot more going on and people need answers. Based on my own experience and close scrutiny of up-to-date research, I really feel that people are actually suffering from adrenal function problems both back then and today.

Adrenal function problems

The adrenal glands are found on top of the kidneys and are a vital part of the endocrine system. They produce several important hormones and are essential for the body to deal with stress. The glands have two parts: the cortex and the medulla. The cortex is the outer layer of the gland and produces a powerful hormone called cortisol. Cortisol can increase blood pressure and blood sugar in response to stress and helps to control inflammation. The level of cortisol in the body directly affects allergies, wound healing, and conditions such as asthma, arthritis and lupus, etc. The inner part of the adrenal gland called the medulla produces two important hormones: epinephrine (adrenaline) and norepinephrine.

These hormones are responsible for speeding up the body's metabolism when coping with stress. They are responsible for the 'fight or flight' response to danger and stress and are part of the nervous system. The adrenal glands are also linked to two structures in the brain called the hypothalamus and the pituitary gland.

Prolonged stress, poor diet, overconsumption of sugar and refined carbohydrates, overuse of caffeine, alcohol, drugs and nicotine as well as deficiencies in vitamin B and C can all contribute to impaired adrenal function. Therefore, if a person is easily prone to allergies and infections, feels cold and is constantly drained and exhausted, suffers from low blood sugar and blood pressure, then it may be due to adrenal problems. I see many young sports people who suffer the same symptoms and, as a former executive of the Clare County Board, I am glad to see that the GAA are finally beginning to realise the effects that overtraining is having on these young people.

When you begin to understand just how the body functions and how it reacts to pressure, you can then take the various steps to prevent these serious health problems. This will result in a remarkable improvement in your health, thereby allowing you to avoid a life of misery. I cannot emphasise this enough – it is all about being responsible. Psychological assessment, antidepressants and sleeping pills are of little use in the long run. In fact, too much sleep is of no value to your body or energy system. What happens is that over a period of time you can become addicted to your disease.

Addiction

The biggest addiction out there at the moment is not alcohol or drugs but negative thoughts. A negative attitude is the kind of addiction that is more destructive than anything else because it can often lead to other addictions, such as alcoholism and drug abuse. However, addictions can be cured and again science has proven this. What we know is that the brain responds to patterns in our life. If you are all the time repeating a particular pattern of lifestyle, then the nerve cells of the brain fire and wire together that pattern. You create this neural network in the brain that is like a web that reminds you of your need for more alcohol, more chocolate, more drugs or whatever the addiction may be. Do you honestly think the brain knows the difference between a glass of wine and a glass of water? It does not. It is just responding to what you are doing.

By using subliminal CDs, working with the energy system and encouraging different habits, then we can effectively treat people with such problems by rewiring their system. If every day, you have a pain in your back, your system goes into a negative cycle and this cycle will present itself every day. However, when you decide to change, when you decide to start exercising, making changes to your diet, adopting a more positive outlook, doing things differently, the brain will change in accordance with your new plan. It is waiting for you to get up and say: 'Right that's it, I'm finished with this type of lifestyle, this type of experience, and I'm going to change right now.' Once you make that conscious decision, your brain will pick it up, and eventually you will start breaking up that old neural network and recreating a whole new network of health. Once you begin to feel better, then you start *believing* you can feel better. Once the belief kicks in, it starts a whole new habit and so the brain rewires itself according to this way of thinking. As a result, the body recovers and responds. This is not a fanciful idea; this is what happens to people in our clinics.

Tapping into your creativity

We have an education system designed solely for the academic, and so we are not educated in ways to tap into our creativity. When you do not train children to tap into their own creative abilities, they get lost in the whole structure of education, and many end up leaving school because it simply does not provide for them. As you already know, I left school at the age of fifteen. Although I subsequently attended college, it was only later in my life that I was drawn to study. Prior to that, however, I could not see school as providing the help I needed, as it simply did not offer an outlet for my creativity.

If you force children into an academic situation, you are going to see a breakdown, with children revolting against society more and more as they grow older. Fortunately, however, research is now focusing on the matter in greater detail. Scientists have begun to examine why some people go on to obtain diplomas, degrees and doctorates and yet make nothing of themselves and not realise their potential, while people who drop out of education in their early teenage years often go on to become leaders in society. How did those future leaders fall through the cracks? It is because sometimes the creativity just simply is not recognised in the early years.

Every day, children should be learning ways of meditation. This is happening in other countries, and it should most certainly be happening here in Ireland. It is absolutely pivotal that we empower our children from the beginning. It is no good telling the youth that they are useless or good for nothing, which is unfortunately a habit in Irish society. We need to educate them, give them leadership qualities, make them responsible for themselves and make them appreciate that their life should not be judged on the basis of their exam results or their academic qualifications. Children and adolescents need this type of stimulation and if they get it – if they are exposed to the great things they can achieve – then a lot of potential problems will be eliminated in society.

Interestingly, parents always notice that when their children have bio-energy treatment, the children are much calmer. Even women who receive the treatment during pregnancy notice that their newborn baby is very placid and calm. In fact, the birth itself is often much more relaxed. There is vast potential for bio-energy therapy to be used as a method of prevention.

While it would be wonderful for people to embrace and encourage the creativity in children, it is never too late for they themselves to tap into their own creativity. After all, creativity is a part of who we are from the day we are born until the day we die. There is no time limit on it, so do not use your age as an excuse to avoid it. I see men and women of around ninety years of age and upwards coming into my clinics for energy treatment. In the context of energy, there is no such thing as age limits or time limits; there is just the present moment. You can make the decision right now – do you want to spend the rest of your life creating problems, diseases and negativity, or do you want to stop that right now and use that same energy to become a happier, healthier and all-round better person? If you want a better quality of life, then you need to train your brain into feeling that way and your body will soon respond.

If you are finding this process difficult at the beginning, then this is where the energy treatment will come in useful. When a Plexus bio-energy therapist works with the patient's energy, the treatment will initiate the whole process for the patient because it alters the negative frequency in the energy system, thereby allowing the person to relax. The person is connecting to the cause of the disease and, as a result, is able to overcome it. Our treatment stimulates the change that allows the patient to disconnect energetically from the specific experiences that initially caused the disease. This is exactly the kick-start people need.

I truly believe that as long as you stifle the creativity of a human being, you are going to create doubt, fear, anxiety and lack of vision. Ireland has been great for producing some remarkable visionaries, but it has always taken the individual to do it. It is simply not inherent in our culture. As a society, we do not tend to encourage optimism, ambition or creativity and this is actually quite sad. In America, there is that general feeling that anyone can live the dream if they are willing to get up and make it happen for themselves. In Ireland, however, people are almost afraid to make it happen.

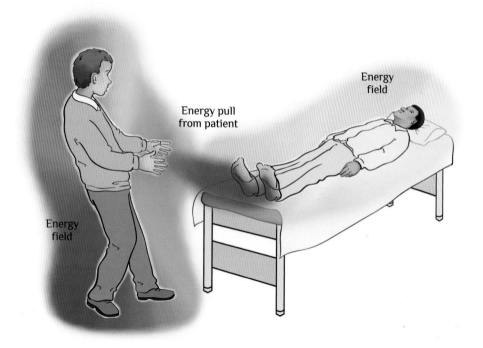

Guidance and leadership

As I stated earlier, disease is an attempt to draw our awareness to the real problem. Likewise, the disease within the economic situation in 2009 is an attempt to draw our awareness to the core problem of society. We have no leadership. You could ask anyone in the country to choose a political role model in Ireland that would be capable of leading us out of this situation, but the reality is that there is no one. There is no one individual who has the spiritual and charismatic personality to not only talk to the people and reassure them that everything will be okay, but to follow this up with positive actions.

From Ireland's history, Michael Collins is the only person I can think of who had such abilities. I choose him not because of his political views but because of the energy he possessed. Collins was able to motivate people: he was an individual with amazing energy, charisma and spirituality. Collins embodied all the characteristics that people seek in a leader. If confronted with today's situation in Ireland, I think he would now do exactly what he did back then. He would motivate people by getting out there and talking to them. He would guide them towards finding positive solutions. I do not believe we would have ever seen him govern in anger, because Collins was the sort of person who would have recognised the various problems and adapted to the situation as it went on. Just as he did back in the 1920s, he would empower the people because that is the only way to move forward in a progressive manner.

> *Twenty years from now you will be more disappointed by the things that you didn't do than by the ones you did do. So throw off the bowlines. Sail away from the safe harbour. Catch the trade winds in your sails. Explore. Dream. Discover.*
>
> *Mark Twain*

The politicians nowadays, regardless of political party, are not leaders. They all say the right things, but the problem is that their words are not making our society healthier or happier. We still have a very sick society. All you have to do is look at the statistics to see that disease, suicide and addictions are all on the increase. You may ask why I am even making reference to this, but I feel compelled to, as it is this lack of leadership and vision at the top that filters down the line and creates a vibration for illness in our society.

What goes around comes around...

On the wall in my office hangs a painting of an old Indian chief known as Chief Seattle. Underneath his picture are words he wrote back in 1854: 'All things are connected. Whatever befalls the earth, befalls the sons of the earth. Man did not weave the web of life, he is merely a strand in it. Whatever he does to the web, he does to himself.' Chief Seattle's last line in particular supports my belief that what you give out will come back to you; what goes around comes around. No matter what way you say it, it all means the one thing. Karma.

We can all have our own experience of karma. During the boom years, I could have been charging colossal sums but I never did. I never took advantage of the situation or exploited the economic circumstances. These days, multinational companies, who perhaps were guilty of exploitation at some stage, are exiting the country at a rapid rate. Fortunately, however, I find my business going from strength to strength and I have no doubt in my mind that it is all down to good karma.

There are people who visit my clinic and who sometimes may not be able to afford the treatment. When I see their situation, I simply will not charge them. In fact, I will often show the partner of the patient exactly how to work with the energy themselves rather than having them feel that the therapy is another financial burden to bear. If it means I can use the opportunity to teach them and make their lives easier, then I do not mind. I am not saying we must all try to be perfect. After all, it is part of human nature that we are going to do negative things, but if our lives are predominantly positive then good things are going to come our way.

In our attempts to live a good life or to fulfil a particular ambition, we tend to first look towards individuals whom we deem to be inspiring role models. We see these people as a representation of the goal we wish to achieve. While for the most part, this can be a good thing, I firmly believe that people should never idolise the icons of pure materialism that adorn both the business and social pages of our newspapers. To do so is to set yourself up for a fall. Forget looking to the media spotlight when it comes to choosing role models. Businessmen, supermodels, actors, socialites, and so on, may lead what appears to be a charmed existence, but what you see on the glossy pages of the magazines is not an accurate reflection of their reality.

Fortunately, there is a new religion emerging and it is the religion of responsibility. This in turn will inspire a major reawakening. For example, if you are unemployed, do not sit around in pessimistic gloom. Use it as an opportunity to tap into your creativity. Deal with the reality and do not waste your time making excuses. It is very easy to blame your unemployment on the economy but those excuses will not improve your situation, so why bother voicing them in the first place? Instead, do what I outlined in the earlier stages of this chapter. Channel your energy into changing your perception. Don't lie around; get up and go for a walk.

There is work out there and there are many opportunities. The nature of the work you find may not be what you envisioned yourself doing, but it may be the best thing that ever happened to you. People are now looking at their own situations and wondering what they will do, but the best thing they can possibly do at this point is to become creative. If you are unemployed, then treat this as your wake-up call.

I have always been a naturally optimistic person, and there have been more than one or two occasions where I have looked back and wondered where it came from. I saw my parents rear ten children with nothing and it made me think. If they could do all that with so few resources at their disposal, then what could I do for myself? That is where my optimism and motivation comes from. It stems back to how I was brought up. Once my siblings and I were able to walk, we were in the bog helping with the turf or whatever, or else out in the garden digging or just generally working in some way. That was the life we knew. We had to get up, get out and do it. And I like to think I have carried that with me all through my life and will continue to do so.

If you want to make things happen, you too have got to get up, get out and do it. If you make this your mantra and act on it, then you are destined for better things in life. We can all see now that during the good times, we completely lost touch. Back when I was a kid, people did not have mobile phones or niceties; they had three bedrooms and ten children. Suddenly this Celtic Tiger came pounding into our lives and within a millisecond people had ten bedrooms and three children. We allowed our lives to spiral. For some people, it was not enough to simply buy a designer shirt, they had to buy it in every colour. With such a money-orientated mentality, we were doomed to fail.

When you see life for what it truly is, and realise we are in this world to evolve as spiritual beings, nature will always try to keep you on track. If you deviate from that, disease is likely to set in. Listen to what your body is telling you and give it the care and attention it needs. You are the one who will benefit most.

REMEMBER

Disease is merely an attempt to draw our attention to a part of our being that we are ignoring.

Testimony of Anne Livingstone

How my arthritis was cured.

Anne Livingstone from County Clare is certainly more than au fait with the meaning of pain after having suffered from a severe form of rheumatoid arthritis. In fact, the pain was so bad at one stage that even simple things such as sleeping and walking posed great difficulty. In her testimony, Anne recalls how the bio-energy treatment sessions freed her from the grips of this debilitating condition.

'Considering how much pain I was in two years ago, I would describe the change as dramatic,' declares Anne. 'In fact, I'd even go so far as to call it a miracle. I was suffering from rheumatoid arthritis at the time and I could barely leave the house I was in so much pain. I couldn't walk that far, just around the house and naturally this made life very difficult.

'It was a friend of mine that first mentioned Michael's name to me and suggested I go see him. I was having acupuncture at the time but I didn't find it helping my condition, so I figured I'd have nothing to lose by paying a visit to Michael's clinic. After my friend discussed with me the kind of treatment that was involved, she went ahead and made the appointment on my behalf. I just wanted to get rid of the pain and frankly I'd have tried anything.

'I went into his clinic for a four-day treatment session. As he was working on me, I could actually feel the sensation of pain travelling down through my legs and knees and leaving my body through my toes. I literally felt the pain going away. Before I left, Michael told me I could come back for another treatment session if I felt I needed it. I took him up on this because I found that the more I went back for treatment, the better I felt.

'There was a noticeable change in my condition. Before undergoing the energy treatment, I was practically eating painkillers. They would temporarily deaden the pain but they would never eliminate it. My life was very much affected by the arthritis. I would even go so far as to say it took over my life. I could barely walk, I couldn't leave the house and I couldn't sleep. After the initial treatments, I only needed to return once every six months or whenever I felt I needed it.

'I wasn't sceptical about the treatment process because I already believed in healers and their healing abilities. Looking back, I do think having an open mind and a positive attitude helped my situation. My family was certainly left very shocked by the change in my condition. In fact, I actually dread to think how much pain I would be in today had I not undergone the treatment when I did.'

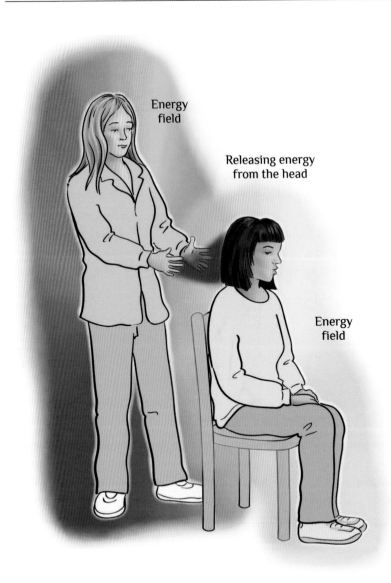

Energy field

Releasing energy from the head

Energy field

5

Emotions

Often people assume that all they have to do in order to live a happier life is think positive thoughts. What they do not realise, however, is that positive thoughts are absolutely useless unless they are accompanied by positive feelings. In actual fact, a person would be far better off thinking negative thoughts and having positive feelings than thinking positive thoughts and having negative feelings. Yes, it may seem confusing and hard to believe, but it is a reality supported by science. You see, the body does not react with a thought, it reacts with a feeling. For example, you cannot think grief without feeling it. When you experience the death of a loved one, you think about that person but the emotion that you are feeling is grief. The thinking goes on in the head, but the emotion itself is played out in the body.

The key, however, is to be able to identify which emotions relate to which parts of your body. This is by no means a concept built from whimsical notions of new age thinking. In fact, in most Eastern cultures, people are already very much aware of how emotions are stored within the organs. Think about it. If a person is nervous all the time, they tend to run to the toilet quite a lot. This is because the emotion of fear is stored within the kidneys and the bladder. Love, meanwhile, is expressed through the heart, because the heart organ is where the emotion of love is contained. As the opposite of love is hate, people who harbour much impatience, hate and resentment will find that their heart energy centre is affected. Feelings of grief and loss are actually divided between the heart and the lungs. The grief associated with losing a loved one is stored in the heart, while depression and anxiety is stored specifically in the lungs. Our emotions also have sounds and colours. This is why if someone has a problem with their liver, it is reflected in the yellow colour of their skin due to bilirubin. Once you try to see the relationship between your emotions and your organs, you will then understand precisely how your mental health directly impacts upon your physical health.

I want people to move on from this chapter knowing that no matter how poor their quality of life might be right now, how depressed or down they are, it can always be overcome. If you doubt my statement, then answer this next question. Is it not better to spend the rest of your life trying to change for the better than to spend it feeling depressed about your current situation? Every day I see people in my clinic consciously swimming in a cesspool of negative emotions powerless to move forward simply because they do not know how to connect to or transform their emotions. Drugs are not the answer and never will.

In Ireland today, we hear so much about the things that are going wrong. Unemployment figures are rising, stock markets are reportedly about as healthy as our hospitals, companies are going into liquidation, and so on and so forth. When all those negative factors are combined, however, it results in the creation of a vast amount of negative feeling within society towards the economy. Unfortunately, due to the various economic occurrences that have taken place in Ireland over the past year, we as a nation are left with an epidemic of destructive emotions, one of which is worry. Worry in particular is a highly destructive emotion. It affects the spleen energy, which can then compromise the effectiveness of the digestive system. This, according to Dr Stephen Gascoigne in *The Manual of Conventional Medicine for Alternative Practitioners*, results in Crohn's disease and digestive disorders as well as chronic bronchitis, eczema, psoriasis, headaches and skin conditions.

Once we give people the tools and specific techniques they need in order to transform worry – and assuming they take these on board – their body will stop producing excess mucus and their digestive system will begin to function properly again. Consequently, waste does not build up in their digestive system and does not end up having to be excreted through their skin as such. Hence, they are not at risk of eczema and psoriasis. Their energy levels also increase and overall the individual feels better.

It is understandable that some people cannot help but worry, but this is even more reason for them to try and find ways of transforming it. In order for a person to do this, they need to first realise the implications of their worrying. Once they understand and acknowledge why they need to change, then all they have to do is actively work on interrupting their thoughts of worry and, above all, their feelings of worry. For example, if you have a deadline at work, the worry about not reaching that deadline will create an anxiety about the situation. The anxiety then affects the frontal lobe of the brain, and so your decision-making and your clarity become affected. This is why you will often notice that when a person is worried or stressed, they tend to rub the front of their forehead. They probably do not realise that what they are actually doing is stimulating the frontal lobe of their brain and relaxing the bones of the skull to try to regain some clarity in their thinking. The key, however, is to first forget about the problem, or in this case, the deadline. Just accept that everything will be fine and that you will have everything done. Now that you have interrupted the feeling of anxiety and replaced it with one of calm, you will end up completing your work in half the time. This is because your mind, your brain and your feelings are not preoccupied with thoughts of the deadline. By taking every minute as it comes, this will result in you becoming more relaxed and producing better results.

For people with conditions like obsessive compulsive disorder (OCD), the idea of one day conquering their problem may seem like a pipe dream. In reality, however, OCD is nothing more than a programme consisting of worry, fear and insecurity. It is a combination of emotions that ultimately stem from a total lack of security in a person's life. OCD is an addiction but, like all addictions, I believe it can be changed. Sufferers simply need to realise that they must interrupt the thought as it occurs. When they begin to think 'I must make sure that cup is left in a certain way', they must force themselves to stop and repeat the words, 'I don't need to change it'. They must then go and find something to do in order to keep themselves distracted until the obsessive feeling passes. Once you keep interrupting the thoughts in this way, the brain will suddenly start to rewire itself. It will start to secrete different hormones that will subsequently result in the person becoming more relaxed. Over a period of time, working with the energy is the most effective way to completely overcome these problems.

Did you know that 90 per cent of the cells in a human being are microorganisms, fungi and bacteria, not human cells? This is all part of nature working together. We have to begin to trust in nature not drugs. So I believe when we correct the energy imbalance that the body and mind can heal naturally. By the very fact of nature alone, we are worriers and emotionally driven beings. Even so, it is only when we allow the negative emotions to become predominant that we develop problems and confronting those emotions with drugs can create a lot more problems. We are powerful individuals capable of achieving anything; we just need to get in touch with that belief and put it to good use.

As you already know from Pat and Margaret Roche's story, an emotion affects the energy system by freezing it in the moment of the experience. Over a period of time, if this is not corrected or brought back into balance, eventually the person's body will suffer as a result. This imbalance may manifest itself in the form of depression, anxiety, back pain, digestive problems, headaches or tiredness. The person may even suffer from a combination of these ailments, not to mention various types of fears and phobias, which also result from an imbalance. Overall, it has the ability to create a huge kink in the armour of the human being.

Some time ago, I hosted a talk in Ireland about the connection between energy and disease. I will never forget the two people who approached me afterwards and told me why they could clearly identify with everything I had said on stage. They started by telling me about a relation of theirs who had been diagnosed with ovarian cancer, which then spread to the heart area. Sadly, they said she was now simply waiting to die. After reflecting on their relation's life, they realised that she had never recovered from the death of her son some years earlier. Her failure to recover from this grief had, I believe, manifested itself in her body as cancer. Think back to what I told you earlier regarding the connection between disease and the organs, and now apply it to this particular situation. We associate the ovaries with reproduction and the creation of a child, and this is precisely where the woman's cancer began in the years following the loss of her son. It then spread to her heart, which as we know, is where the emotion of love is stored.

As long as the shock, trauma and grief of the experience remains stored within the body it will manifest itself in disease. This is simply because the energy blockage was never released in order to allow the body to recover in the first place. I know from my own experience of my father's death that the worst thing anyone can say is 'get up and get on with it'. In fact, for three years after his death, I went through turmoil because I chose to get up and get on with it. I did this primarily by immersing myself in my work. Fortunately, I came to my senses and realised I needed to address the problem. In doing so, I underwent energy work along with grief counselling and confiding in close friends. It was this combination of critical factors that brought me back to 100 per cent health. The silver line to emerge from this despondent period of my life is that I can now completely identify with people who suffer from depression and grief. I know from my own experience of turmoil that you simply cannot get up and get on with life. You have to first deal with the emotion associated with the experience. Correcting the energy system is of critical importance to a person's recovery from depression. That said, so too are other factors such as exercise, diet and natural supplements for depression.

If something happened in your life – be it recently or some years ago – and that incident still sits at the back of your mind, or as we see it, frozen in your energy system, then it is imperative that you commence the process of letting go or transforming it. Of course, you cannot let go of the problem by hiding it deeper in your subconscious. You must face up to it, deal with it, and then you can move on. If however you do not know how to effectively deal with your problem, then the energy work carried out by the therapist will help you to begin the process. Imagine the therapist defrosting your body of stagnant, frozen or blocked energy and any shock resulting from an experience. Once this is complete, your body will start to relax. You then adopt certain responsibilities to continue the good work, such as breathing exercises, visual techniques, emotional transformation techniques, an improved diet and physical exercise.

Reader, you may assume the things that lurk in your mind are just not major enough to bring about sickness. Let me assure you, if unresolved matters still rest in your mind, then they will manifest themselves in ill-health. Believe it or not, even something like a bad break-up can prove detrimental to your state of health in the distant future. The majority of us have at some stage in our lives experienced the break-up of a relationship. However, if a person goes through a particularly bad break-up and does not deal with it properly, then they will undoubtedly be affected by it again sometime in their future. It will most likely manifest itself in health problems relating to the heart and other organs. The emotion of love is stored in the heart energy centre.

You see when it comes to energy, it makes no difference whether it is a break-up, a trauma, or just a painful memory. If you do not suitably deal with the issue that is causing you anxiety, then it is going to return in some form to remind you that it is still waiting to be acknowledged. I always maintain that having a problem on your mind is like having a pebble in your shoe; although the pebble may be small, it is enough to stop you walking. If you are going around every day with a metaphorical pebble in your shoe, it will stop you from moving forward. This will continue to be the case until your energy system is restored to its natural balance. We re-empower the patient by helping them to disconnect energetically from the experience that has caused them the problem. This allows the body an opportunity to recover. You have to remember, healing is a process.

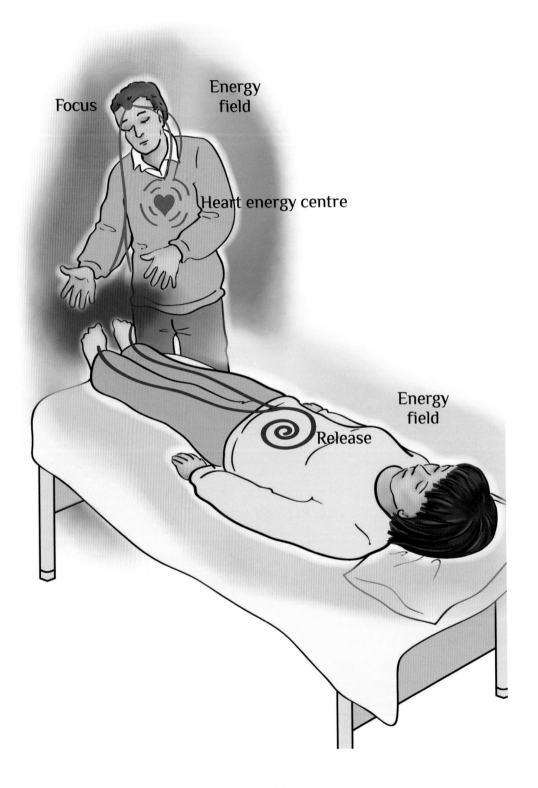

Depression

Depression, in my opinion, is a general medical term that covers a multiple of negative emotions. There is little incentive, I believe, within the medical system to cure depression or any other disease for that matter. Why? Because pharmaceutical companies are simply making too much money from it. Sickness is a big business and that is the bottom line. If you think right now that some multinational drug company has staff working in some lab looking for ways to cure your problems, then you are living an illusion. They are looking for ways to treat the problem not cure it. It can sometimes happen that patients with a chronic illness can develop depression and often time it is the medication they are on for this condition that has induced this depressive state, given that depression is a side-effect to some drugs.

Some people never find a way out of this debilitating state because they are not thinking independently or feeling for themselves. They are simply reacting to an environment that is totally alien to a human being. Due to being chemically stimulated with sleeping pills, antidepressants, relaxation drugs and so forth, the person becomes nothing more than an observer of their own life. Certainly, those with conditions such as schizophrenia, psychosis, etc. need medical intervention. But should this be the case for the rest of their lives? I would say perhaps not, if they do not want it to be. As I have stated in previous chapters, if a person believes something to be a reality then that is exactly what the outcome will be. I want you to take much from this book, but if you only take one thing with you, then let it be the following: what a person perceives, a person creates. Fortunately, however, what science has taught us is that we do not need to be depressed or sick for the rest of our lives.

Depression is basically a complete blockage in the energy system that allows no light into the body. Due to this blockage, many negative hormones are secreted in the body, which then results in the body being pulled down. Over a period of time, a person suffering from depression develops a habit where they are continuously telling themselves, almost convincing themselves, that they are feeling tired, down, stressed, cannot sleep and have no energy. By engaging in this line of thinking, the person is essentially programming their brain into thinking negatively; they are actively encouraging it into a depressed state. While all this is going on, the brain is not only listening to the information, it is also storing every detail it is being fed. It then wires both itself and the body based on what you are thinking and feeling. Remember, thoughts on their own do not bear much of an impact. It is the energy from the feeling and from the emotion associated with the thought that creates the blockage.

Just as the OCD sufferer must interrupt their habit in order to fight their disorder, the key to breaking hold of negative thoughts is to begin interrupting the thought in question. However, it is pivotal that you carry out this 'interruption process' on a continual basis because, as we already know, the nerve cells that do not fire together will not wire together. If you change your pattern of thinking, your feelings and your emotions, you end up replacing the old with the new. As a result, you start to rewire your body in a completely new and improved way. When your cells start to pick up on this new information, your body inherits the details both biologically and physiologically, and consequently the disease leaves your system.

There are many ways to go about achieving this. For many, reciting affirmations is the first port of call. While this is an acceptable method, the problem with affirmations is that people tend to learn them off and then simply repeat them. They *say* the affirmation but they do not *feel* the emotion that should accompany it. Think about it. It is a complete waste of time saying 'I'm healthy, happy and secure in my future' if you do not *feel* anything while saying it. All you are simply doing is talking. You have to feel healthy and happy; you have to connect to the feeling. When you are told to 'be positive', I bet you immediately associate that concept with the idea of absorbing as many optimistic thoughts as you can muster. Yet after days of feeding yourself these 'lifelines', you wonder why you are not even beginning to feel an improvement. Well, now you know. Negative feelings counteract positive thoughts. That is the problem encountered by most people when they choose affirmations as a means of rewiring their system. Every day, they reel off their rehearsed list of affirmations before eventually giving up out of sheer frustration over the lack of positive change in their life. Sometimes people simply forget to say their daily affirmations after the first few days have passed when the zeal of the newly reformed has worn off.

If you go out and ask people what they are thinking, you will find that most will be thinking positively. However, if you immediately follow it up with a question on how they are feeling about the future, the same people will most likely respond with a statement about how desperate the country is at the moment and how bad the job crisis is. Like I said, you can think positive all you like, but it is the feeling positive part that you need to put into practice.

When a person arrives at our clinic seeking treatment for depression, it could be the result of any number of factors – stresses at work, at home, or problems they had as a child. Regardless of what the source may be, we know there is no one thing that is going to solve that problem – there is no miracle cure but the miracle is achievable through hard work. Our approach to psychological complaints is the same as our approach to those of a physical nature. We identify the problem and then carry out our work with the energy system. Once this step is completed, we re-educate the patient through methods such as the use of subliminal music, which is designed to change the information in the subconscious. We also teach the patient how to connect with their emotions and understand the relationship between their organs and their emotions. More importantly, however, we teach them how to transform their negative emotions into those of a more positive variety.

We prefer deploying a programme of recovery because we know it will not lead to the patient suffering more problems in the future, which would be the case if they were on prescribed medication. The wonderful thing about working with the energy is that it disconnects the patient energetically from the experience that brought about their depression in the first place. It does not make them forget the incident; it just unfreezes that 'frozen-in-time' feeling. By working with the energy, we can clear that energy blockage in the organs and give the patient a new start. Even so, the patient has got to take everything on board and continue the habit of positive feelings in order to gain maximum benefit from the treatment. People must start removing themselves from the destructive mentality where they limit their options to either medication or miracle. They assume these two options are the only two that will free them from disease, but, take it from me, this line of thinking almost always leads to disappointment.

When people become sick, their first port of call is usually the doctor's surgery. However, when the doctor cannot do anything for them, they suddenly seek a miracle cure. What I would like to know is where did that idea even come from? Why do we believe the notion that if the doctors fail, then the situation calls for a miracle cure? That is absolutely ridiculous. Just because medical science cannot cure your problem does not mean there are not several other avenues you can exhaust. If a doctor cannot provide a solution to your condition, it is not the end of the road. There are many other options available; many more routes you can try. Just keep working at it in as relaxed a manner as possible, while at the same time maintaining a positive focus and perception of things. It may sound clichéd, but you really will be amazed at what your mind can achieve.

Unfortunately, people are led to believe that a doctor's word is the only word. Bearing this in mind, it is no surprise that when an individual receives an unfavourable diagnosis or perhaps a negative update on their condition, they end up severely depressed and anxious about the situation. They are possibly supplied with prescription drugs and in some cases told they will have to remain on those drugs for the rest of their lives. The person becomes very down about things, but only because they have taken on board the perception of their future based on the medical opinion voiced by their doctor. I know I have repeated this statement several times already in this chapter, but I simply cannot emphasise it enough – what a person believes, a person creates. Once people start to take this fact on board, then and only then will we see a reduction in the number of people losing their lives to disease. It will also spell the end of a person's reliance on medication. On this point, have you ever considered just how many people end up in hospital every year because of the side-effects of drugs? Ever questioned just how many people overdose on antidepressants? There is a considerable increase in both suicide and attempted suicide, yet there is also a big increase in the prescribing of antidepressants. Remarkably, it all goes totally unchecked.

I remember speaking with a woman who had suffered from depression for nineteen years. Considering her condition had not improved, I voiced my opinion that all the medication she had been taking was clearly not working. At that, she informed me that while she had previously taken medication specifically for depression, she was now on drugs for schizophrenia, even though she believed she did not suffer from the condition. Was she hearing voices? No, but she was hearing sounds. When people are emotionally stressed, they become hypersensitive; their thoughts are so real, almost to the point where they start hearing them. In fact, people who are hypersensitive are simply accessing other parts of their consciousness. In this particular case, the woman had been transferred to a psychiatrist who had treated her like she were mad, medicating her for all those years. If we as a society do not actively begin to develop a greater understanding of our bodies and how we can protect them from disease, then we will undoubtedly encounter far greater problems down the road. There needs to be a change in perspective, and I sincerely hope this book will ignite that change.

In the last chapter, I spoke about addictions and how the biggest and most harmful addiction currently manifesting itself within our society is that of negative thoughts, visions and perceptions. I have no doubt that it is within these emotions that we find the recipe for all disease. When people become addicted to such a despondent way of thinking, the brain picks up on this information. It creates a neural network whereby the hypothalamus at the centre of the brain produces neurohormones based on our thinking, our perceptions and our feelings. When this occurs, hormones are sent to the pituitary gland and into the bloodstream where they then stimulate cells. This activity creates a change in the information already being stored within the cell, causing a detrimental effect. After that, it is only a matter of time before the organs become sick as well. The symptoms that emerge from harbouring negative emotions can range from bronchial-type problems to digestive disorders, arthritic conditions, fatigue and headaches, even cancer. When a person develops these symptoms, they inevitably end up feeling tired, which can very often result in a vicious love triangle with stimulants. The usual suspects are coffee, energy drinks, alcohol and junk food. That said, there is another form of dangerous stimulant that we seek out depending on the nature of the emotion we are feeling.

If the type of emotion that you are constantly feeling has negative and attention-seeking traits, then you will simply attract a variety of situations and experiences that stimulate that emotion. Whenever I talk about this topic, the example I always use is of the woman who marries the alcoholic. She subsequently separates from her husband but ends up with another alcoholic for a partner. This is because she keeps attracting this situation to her life. She does not even realise it, but the situation in question is what stimulates her addiction of negative thinking. You can probably guess what happens next. The woman ends up paying a visit to her doctor and walks out with a prescription for some form of antidepressant. She may view the pills as a solution to her problem but the fact of the matter is that her addiction to negative thinking and living will still weigh her down until she deals with it properly.

We need to develop a relationship with ourselves, create our own personality and identity, if not we are doomed to rely on others for our love and happiness. You must realise that you can only find the divine, love and happiness within yourself not outside or in someone else. You need to go internal.

Living in the attic of our consciousness

Imagine buying a brand new house. Now imagine living in the attic of your new house every single day for thirty years. Upon emerging from the attic after such duration, in what condition would you expect to find your house? This is how I demonstrate the problem in society at the moment. We are living in the

Seven layers of energy field

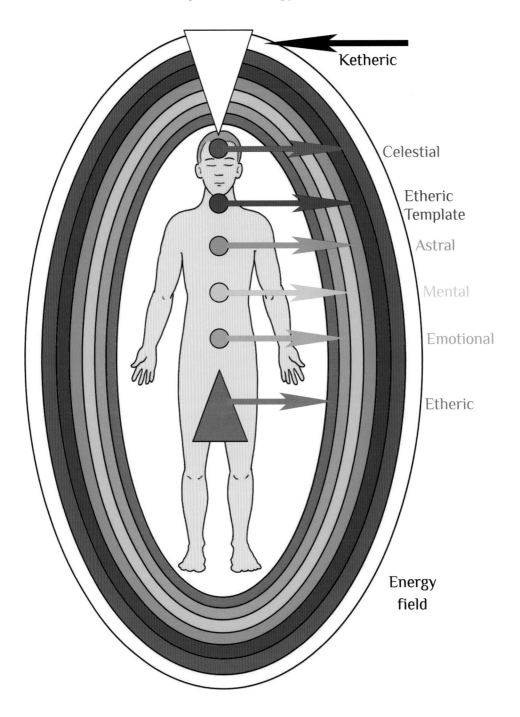

Ketheric

Celestial

Etheric
Template

Astral

Mental

Emotional

Etheric

Energy
field

attics of our bodies – basically, we are living in our heads. Eighty-five per cent of our positive thinking is worthless because we simply do not follow it up with positive feeling.

Many of you reading this may not be suffering from chronic depression. In fact, you may not even be depressed; you are just plodding along through life yet feeling as though you could be so much happier. Do you realise that you are feeling this way because, just like the patient with chronic depression, you too have a blockage of energy in your system? The strength of your depression is irrelevant because it all boils down to the one thing. A blockage of the energy.

> *Go confidently in the direction of your dreams. Live the life you have imagined.*
>
> Henry David Thoreau

It is impossible to place a figure on the number of people suffering from depression as so many people struggle with it in silence. I firmly believe that the greatest challenge to every human being is to find true peace, contentment and happiness. Unfortunately, however, the chemical formula for happiness simply does not exist. This means that whether we like it or not, we simply have to accept that we cannot be happy all the time. What people need to realise is that as long as they exist in the illusion that they must be happy all the time, then the opposite result is what will be achieved – the feeling of sadness will end up presiding in their lives. Sadness, guilt, happiness, hatred, resentment, fear, love, patience, impatience and anger are all the natural reactions to events in our lives. Until we accept this, we are always going to be seeking what is not there to seek.

In this lifetime, we are going to experience every sort of emotion. The good news, however, is that the predominant emotion can indeed be happiness, love and compassion. On the other hand, the biggest and most powerful emotion that we need to understand and embrace is forgiveness. If a person is angry, bitter or resentful, it is because they cannot forgive. Think about it. When we cannot forgive ourselves, we become self-destructing. When we cannot forgive our neighbour, our employer or our friend, for whatever reason, we become bitter and angry. It is the lack of forgiveness that creates the problems and this is another fact of life that people just need to try and understand more. I find that when I get angry about things, I just say to myself: 'Michael, relax, let it go, it's over, move on.' Learning to cope with disappointments and rejection is another important part of the process. It is incredibly difficult, but in order to feel happier and healthier in the long run, you must learn to do it.

I always believe that people should avoid allowing their moods to go from one extreme to the next – happy one minute, sad the next. Try to achieve a balance by surfing the wave of contentment, happiness and peace. You do this by forgiving whatever it was that caused you that low moment. Forgive the low moment when you experience it so that you do not have to travel further down into the dumps.

People need to escape the notion that they can only find peace, happiness and contentment in another person, as I already mentioned. They cannot and they will not because it is simply not possible. You first have to be happy in your own company. Can you sit down on your own and be happy with your own thoughts and feelings? Do you actually have a relationship with yourself? If you do not at the very least have that, then why would you give another person all your love and compassion to take? It does not make sense. You have to try and develop yourself as a human being, not as a co-dependent partner.

To completely understand this, I want you to envisage two individuals who are madly in love and who tell each other this all the time. Suddenly, however, one half of the couple meets someone else and decides to end the relationship. The other person is distraught, their life is up in a heap, and even after some time has passed they still feel like they have not been right since the break-up. Now put yourself in this person's position and ask yourself why you would feel this way? You feel this way because the other person stole your passion, your care, your love and your energy. However, what you have to realise is that the other person only took this from you because you gave it to them to take.

In relationships, you have to establish and maintain your own identity and personality. If you do not, you are in for a shock if the relationship suddenly disintegrates. This is why I totally disagree with the term 'other half'. I never have and never would refer to my wife Tina as my other half. She is her own person with her own identity just like I am my own person with my own identity. When you learn to be happy with yourself and to appreciate your own identity, then you will have your independence. Consequently, if you ever experience a break-up in life, of course you will react emotionally, but you will be far better equipped to deal with it and move on.

Inner forgiveness is all about forgiving occurrences that happened in the past. This is one thing we find people cannot do; they just have such great difficulty in letting go. In the clinics, however, my therapists teach their patients precisely why they need to learn to let go. Once the patients take this on board, they find ways of dealing with these issues and, as a result, really begin to develop as individuals.

Fortunately, people are beginning to connect with this aspect of their being more and more. It is almost as though society has evolved to a point where they realise that the only person being harmed by their bitterness and resentment is they themselves. Sometimes when people come to the clinic, they bemoan the problems caused by someone like their boss, their husband or their wife. They start firing up and venting their frustration about these problematic individuals in their lives. It is at this point that I will usually step in and ask them to take a look at what they are saying. I simply ask, 'Why are you here because of somebody else? Tell me one person in this world, apart from your own immediate family, that is worth losing a night's sleep over? Tell me one situation in this world that is worth taking sleeping pills for?'

People are prepared to stay in a negative emotionally destructive environment because they feel they lack the power to move out of it. They prefer to stay put because their concern centres on what others are saying about them. It is their lack of belief in themselves that forces them to remain in this situation. When it comes to people like this, their paths are easily predicted. They develop disease from which they will suffer or even die from. Death will literally be their only release from this negativity in their life. Now ask yourself, is this what you want for your life?

Have you ever wondered why it is easier to stay down in the dumps than to be happy? Surely if you could choose, you would pick the option of being happy. So why then is it so much easier to remain in a bad mood than to be in the happy mood you desire? I can tell you exactly why this is the case. It is because you get sympathy; it is your addiction. You are taking energy from someone else. In our clinic, we never resonate at that level; we never engage at the level of consciousness the patient arrives in with. If we start to deliver sympathy, then how can we deliver hope? Our job is to bring the patient to the understanding, the frequency, the perception and the reality of where we want them to be. If by working with their energy, we can bring them to that level, then there is no reason why the person cannot overcome their problems. People have to take responsibility and realise they are going to experience all sorts of emotions. No matter how hard a person tries, they will never completely eliminate anger, resentment, guilt or hatred.

When was the last time you placed your hands over your lungs and silently thanked them for breathing? When was the last time you placed your hands over your liver and thanked it for doing the five hundred different jobs it does in the processing of toxins and keeping you healthy? How about thanking your kidneys, spleen and digestive system? We take it all for granted. Disease is not a stroke of bad luck that entered our lives by chance; it is an attempt to connect us to where our real problems lie – deep within the organ systems, the emotional elements of our being. As you already know, our organ systems contain our emotions. Consequently, any deep-seated or destructive feelings that you harbour will have their consequences.

People are stressed, depressed and are experiencing all kinds of health problems because they are camouflaging and suppressing their negative destructive emotions on a continual basis through drugs, medication and other stimulants. Eventually, however, it will all come back to haunt them. Believe me, I have never seen a case where it does not. Stop living in an illusion and get real. Is it now time you took responsibility for your own life and focus on a future free from disease? Health is your right as a human being; you do not have to suffer. Do not be a statistic. Instead start believing in yourself and leave the past to the past. Come into the moment and project a bright future for yourself. Do not be afraid of your power or your light, embrace them.

REMEMBER

The biggest and most powerful emotion that we need to understand and embrace is forgiveness.

❧ 6 ❧

Children's Health

Apart of my job that I have always really enjoyed is working with children. In this chapter, I hope to explain some of the reasons behind the unfortunate increase in diseases that affect children as well as offer solutions on how they can be overcome.

None of us fully knows whether we were conceived out of love or lust, nor do we know what kind of experience we had in the nine months spent in our mother's womb. As for the type of birth we endured when emerging into the world, no individual can possibly recall if theirs was a traumatic or stressed labour. Remarkably, however, people do not even realise that their conception, womb life and birth have a huge influence on their quality of life and health today. Perhaps you were born by Caesarean section or perhaps your birth involved the use of suction or forceps. Regardless of the measures taken, however, I assure you they have all had an impact on your health.

Autism, ADHD/ADD

When a person does not have any personal experience with conditions such as autism and attention deficit hyperactivity disorder (ADHD)/attention deficit disorder (ADD), they can often find themselves at a loss to understand what such conditions are all about. In essence, when a child has autism or ADHD, it is like they are constantly locked in a subconscious state, depending on the severity. There are stacks upon stacks of medical papers on these conditions, but despite all the research, we are still nowhere close to dealing with why such problems develop in the first place.

I had an opportunity recently to talk to parents about childhood learning and behavioural problems, such as autism and ADHD, and I could see immediately that the frustration experienced by these parents was enormous. A delay in proper diagnosis, treatment and effective services were just some of those frustrations.

There also seems to be many unanswered questions as to the cause of the learning and behavioural problems in children, who by all appearances were perfectly normal at birth. It is just not good enough to put a medical term on these conditions and medicate the sufferers with drugs. The time has come for the Government and medical institutions to carry out proper research to evaluate the possible causes of such problems that our children are experiencing.

I want you to think outside the box a little here. Let us look at the areas that just might be contributing to these problems. This includes genetics and environmental factors and the possible area of vaccines and their safety. There are many parents who steadfastly believe they witnessed a change in their child after they were vaccinated. Is vaccination a possible cause? Much research has been done on the possible link between autism and vaccines, and the medical profession has continuously denied any link. But that changed in 2008 when the Hannah Poling case showed there was a link. The case was reported in the *New England Journal of Medicine* on 15 May 2008 by Dr Paul Offit as follows:

> *On April 11, 2008, the National Vaccine Advisory Committee took an unusual step: in the name of transparency, trust, and collaboration, it asked members of the public to help set its vaccine-safety research agenda for the next 5 years. Several parents, given this opportunity, expressed concern that vaccines might cause autism – a fear that had recently been fueled by extensive media coverage of a press conference involving a 9-year-old girl named Hannah Poling.*

> *When she was 19 months old, Hannah, the daughter of Jon and Terry Poling, received five vaccines – diphtheria-tetanus-acellular pertussis, Haemophilus influenzae type b(Hib), measles-mumps-rubella (MMR), varicella, and inactivated polio. At the time, Hannah was interactive, playful, and communicative. Two days later, she was lethargic, irritable, and febrile. Ten days after vaccination, she developed a rash consistent with vaccine-induced varicella.*

> *Months later, with delays in neurologic and psychological development, Hannah was diagnosed with encephalopathy caused by a mitochondrial enzyme deficit. Hannah's signs included problems with language, communication, and behavior – all features of autism spectrum disorder. Although it is not unusual for children with mitochondrial enzyme deficiencies to develop neurologic signs between their first and second years of life, Hannah's parents believed that vaccines had triggered her encephalopathy. They sued the Department of Health and Human Services (DHHS) for compensation under the Vaccine Injury Compensation Program (VICP) and won.*

On March 6, 2008, the Polings took their case to the public. Standing before a bank of microphones from several major news organizations, Jon Poling said that 'the results in this case may well signify a landmark decision with children developing autism following vaccinations'. For years, federal health agencies and professional organizations had reassured the public that vaccines didn't cause autism and there was no link. Now, with DHHS making this concession in a federal claims court, the government appeared to be saying exactly the opposite.

Did we read anything about this in the Irish newspapers? Have the medics been telling parents that there is a link in susceptible children? Are they taking steps to screen for such problems before they vaccinate these children, and if not are they failing in their duty of care? Parents need answers. If this is the case, then we have to start listening to the parents rather than simply taking the word of those who have a vested interest. While vaccines may be necessary, they are essentially toxic drugs and, as we have stated previously, all drugs have side-effects. Usually parents just accept that vaccines prevent certain diseases, however, they could also be causing other problems. There are many unanswered questions. Could vaccines contribute to toxic shock in susceptible children, thereby resulting in the failure of proper brain integration, affecting learning and behaviour, causing frustration and aggressive behaviour as in the Hannah Polling case? Could vaccines be causing damage to our genetic material thus resulting in more serious health problems in later life? I believe so.

While efforts have been made to make vaccines safe, such as removing mercury from them, more needs to be done. In the USA, the government has already paid out millions to the parents of children who suffered the side-effects of vaccinations. In order to protect their children, parents need to become far more informed and vocal about the components of these vaccines. Parents need answers but, above all, they need to be listened to and provided with the proper support services. I also believe that medicating our children and bringing them to child psychiatrists or psychologists is not the way forward as parents are still left none the wiser. Dr Peter Breggin, a Harvard-trained psychiatrist, stated in the *Sunday Independent* in 2006 that the biggest child abuse currently taking place in our society today is the mass drugging of our children. Are we listening? I guess not.

The present economic climate is having the greatest effect on vital services like applied behavioural analysis (ABA) and special needs assistance in our schools, yet the Government is totally ignoring this growing problem in our society.

Parents now need to become self-sufficient and source other ways of treating their children's health: ways that will enhance their overall development and learning skills. The health of our children has to be foremost in the Government's agenda and they should be judged by same. We have to learn from what is happening in other countries with regard to the medical treatment of children. In America, for example, children are crushing prescribed drugs such as Ritalin for hyperactivity and snorting them. This is a frightening prospect and I firmly believe that in order to prevent it from happening here we need to take every immediate precaution. Rather than creating a foundation for future problems, we need to instead provide meaningful support and services to parents.

Despite the challenges we are faced with, I do have great hope for the future. Parents simply must continue to have hope that living with these problems can be made somewhat easier and that their child can grow up to live a normal and independent life. Love is the basis to all healing, and there is no greater love than the love a parent has for their child. But the medical profession needs to report what they are being told by parents as I feel this is where the real problem lies.

As I write this book I read that the most recent figures on autism from America is that 1 in a 100 and 1 in 60 boys could be affected. An article published in the US news blog, The Huffington Post, by David Kirby on 2 October 2009 relayed the stance adopted by the US government:

> *On October 2 [Washington] confirmed that 1 percent of American children (and by extension, perhaps 1-in-58 boys) has an autism spectrum disorder.... The Secretary [of US Health and Human Services Kathleen Sibelius] declared autism 'an urgent public health challenge,' proclaimed that President Obama was 'right to make it one of our top health priorities,' including research into 'treatments and a cure' for the disorder.*

Since 1990 more than $800 million has been paid out by the US Court of Federal Claims in relation to vaccines, including several with injuries that resulted in 'autism-like symptoms'. Here in Ireland, the Government needs to adopt the same stance as the American government and take steps to deal with this serious health problem. In my opinion, successive governments have failed in their duty to protect our children and it is only a matter of time before the courts rule in favour of victims, as in the Hannah Poling case. Granted there are many factors to take into account from genetics, food, water and air to vaccines, but I feel it is a public scandal that our health service is not taking the proper action. Instead it is leaving it to parents with little or no support. It is now time for the Government to start listening, as the problem will not go away.

Traumatic births

Whenever I talk about the subject of traumatic births in lectures, one of the first topics I refer to is the Caesarean section. As an effective exercise, I often get people to picture an adult sleeping in a warm bed in a dark room. Suddenly, someone throws open the door, rushes in, catches them by the neck and pulls them out. How do you think that person would feel afterwards? Very shocked and traumatised no doubt. They would possibly even require counselling. Now take an unborn child who has been developing safe and sound in their mother's womb for nine months. She is overdue for whatever reason, or there is an emergency, and thus has to be born by Caesarean section. To a child who has just been pulled from the womb, the shock is no different than that experienced by the adult pulled from their bed in the middle of the night. A traumatic birth compromises and weakens the immune system, which in turn leads to problems. While the newborn may be somewhat calmer a short while later, the ripple effect of the trauma they have just experienced will continue well into their life.

I very strongly believe that the shock a child goes through at birth – whether a natural or Caesarean one – has enormous implications to its digestive system, concentration and focus. It is absolutely my opinion that the trauma can contribute to conditions like dyslexia, dyspraxia, anxiety and depression. All we need to do is understand the way the body reacts to stress and the early development of a child to realise this. With this understanding in mind, we see children react positively in our clinics.

Children are thus at risk of developing colic-type symptoms as well as learning and behavioural disorders. This is because the shock and stress of the birth creates a situation whereby negative hormones are released in the body. This forces the baby's muscles, digestive system and cranial bones to tighten. Such pressure is particularly dangerous for the cranial bones as they have not fully developed at this stage nor has the brain been fully integrated.

If there is a significant level of shock and stress experienced at birth, a child can develop what we call a homolateral function. This essentially means that only one side of the brain is functioning. When this occurs, the child's ability to concentrate, focus and learn is hindered. Sometimes the frontal lobe of the brain does not develop properly and is starved of energy. As a result, the left and right sides of the brain do not integrate or communicate properly and this actually forces one side of the body to contort in a certain way. There are several physiological and mechanical reactions that take place in our bodies due to shock and stress; however, I strongly believe we need to take more care when it concerns the birth of a child.

In our clinics, we have treated newborns and children with everything from colic-type symptoms to inconsistent sleeping patterns. What we have found is that after working on the child over a period of a few days, their energy is balanced and the shock frequency is released. As a result, the child leaves the clinic in much better health than when they first arrived.

We also treat conditions such as asthma and other respiratory problems. The common response in a doctor's surgery to these types of symptoms is antibiotics and bronchodilators. Thanks to the seemingly endless supply of antibiotics, we have come across children who may be on up to fifteen courses of antibiotics over a period of eighteen months or less. I think people genuinely do not realise the damage that is being done to children at this point in time. When they become adults, who is to say they will not have behavioural problems, learning disorders, depression or anxiety? Regardless of what the outcome may be, there has to be a reason why these things happen to our children. The key here is to take more care.

Once we work with the energies and get them flowing again, we go about correcting the diet. We then discuss with the parents how they themselves can work with their child to create the right environment in which a full recovery can take place. When shock and stress occurs, the gut bacteria become compromised, but the energy work strengthens the immune system. We then advise parents to give the child proper gut bacteria and introduce the right minerals, vitamins and essential fatty acids into the child's diet as well as teach the parents certain skills in which they can enhance their child's development. There is absolutely no reason why a number of the child's problems cannot be rectified.

Since we began training parents in how to use various techniques on their children, we can see that they too are benefiting enormously. This therapy is not available within the national health system but if our results are anything to go by, then it most certainly should. Parents have to pay privately, but what we want to do is make it more accessible to parents by training them to work with their own children. The healing essentially centres on love, and there is no doubting the love a parent has for their child.

Michael treating a group of children in Chernobyl in the mid-1990s

It may be difficult to understand how a child's time in the womb could result in serious problems later in life, particularly if the mother did not smoke or drink during the pregnancy. Stress, however, can prove to be a huge risk to an unborn child, as can an expectant mother's digestive problems. On the other hand, the mother may not have shown any external symptoms of illness but may just have felt slightly unwell. When the child is born, nonetheless, it may have a digestive compromise resulting in eczema, asthma or respiratory-type problems. This is how the child takes on the problems experienced by the mother. The mother is the mould, the child is the product. The question many expectant mothers need to ask themselves is how are they moulding their unborn children? I truly believe that parental love is the most important thing of all. And all a child needs is love and food. Evidence has even shown that the type of love given to a child has a considerable impact on the growth of the child.

Other childhood diseases

We have so many children being brought to our clinics with conditions such as diabetes, epilepsy, cerebral palsy, etc. If the child is prone to getting seizures, then working with the energy can help reduce the number of seizures the child will experience. In some cases, it can even eliminate them. We see epilepsy as a build-up of electrical activity in the body releasing in the brain through a seizure. When we release this blockage it can have a positive effect on the patient, particularly children who get seizures associated with cerebral palsy. Parents have often told us that when they subsequently take their child to a physiotherapist, the greater elasticity in the muscles and the tendons is usually remarked upon. This is all because of the child having undergone the bio-energy therapy process in our clinics first: a process that works at an energy level that is capable of bringing about change in the child.

As the child is so much more relaxed, there is a greater absorption of nutrients. Once we get the energy system of the child right, we can then assist the process with the basic dynamics, including diet, subliminal music, and certain types of classical music such as Mozart, which is excellent for children. We also use corrective sound treatment such as the Dawson Programme, which we have found to be very effective.

Co-founder of Plexus, Tom Griffin has spent considerable time researching areas of special needs, learning and behavioural disorders. Together we have developed the Plexus special needs programme. We see learning difficulties such as dyslexia and ADHD/ADD affecting thousands of children all over Ireland. These children are awaiting proper assessments with regard to their conditions in the hope that treatment can be provided to enable them to overcome their difficulties. However, conventional methods fall far short of understanding the nature of these conditions

These issues create massive emotional tension for parents and teachers so a new understanding and treatment for these conditions is urgently needed. We address this need in a very effective way with a non-drug approach. This approach, based on twenty years' experience of working in the field of bio-energy, equips us with the understanding of how these conditions can be treated. We believe that these conditions are often the result of trauma at birth or shock afterwards, which in turn creates an imbalance in the electrical/energy systems of the body resulting in bone structure misalignment of the skull and spine. Once this occurs the distribution of information from the left and right brain becomes imbalanced, manifesting as symptoms outlined above. Dyslexia is defined as a learning disorder marked by the impairment of the ability to recognise and comprehend written words causing great frustration and emotional stress both for the child, parents and teachers. We believe that dyslexia is an eyesight problem and has no relationship to the basic intelligence of an individual. The correction of these symptoms is achieved by addressing the underlying physical and emotional electro-physical malfunctions, through leading edge techniques provided within our Plexus clinic. Over the last number of years many children have benefited enormously from this integrated approach, which incorporates parents in the recovery and healing process of these children.

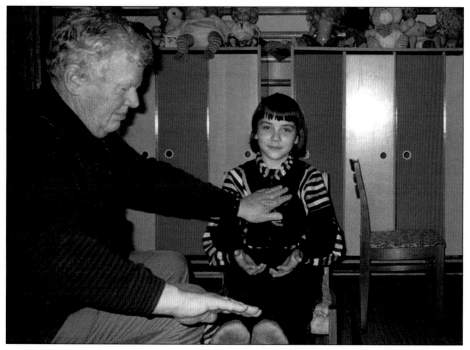

Brian Mooney treating a young girl in Chernobyl

We see children in our clinics with asthma but there are also children with asthmatic symptoms, which is quite different. By this I mean the upper respiratory symptoms are often just down to poor gut flora and excess mucus-forming foods being ingested. By getting the diet and the energy right, there is absolutely no reason why they cannot overcome that problem. Most respiratory problems, be they asthmatic symptoms, sinuses, etc., all come from a compromised digestive system. In *The Manual of Conventional Medicine for Alternative Practitioners*, medical researcher Dr Stephen Gascoigne emphasises the importance of maintaining a strong spleen energy. He states that if spleen energy is depleted for any reason then the gastrointestinal function is compromised, thereby resulting in an overproduction of mucus. This excess mucus collects in the organs and can cause all kinds of problems ranging from bowel disorders to Crohn's disease, ulcerative colitis and even chronic bronchitis if the mucus passes into the lungs. According to Dr Gascoigne, excess mucus can even lodge in the skin, causing eczema. How many doctors tell parents that the spleen energy imbalance can result in such conditions? Once we get the digestive system right, then through working with and correcting both the energy system and the diet, the body can fully recover. That is precisely what happens in our clinics.

It is important that parents of children with diabetes understand and be aware that there will always be implications down the road because insulin has to carefully control the sugar levels. These issues can include anything from circulatory problems to renal failure to eyesight problems, and so forth. As far as I am concerned, children's health is not fully understood. Parents need to know that there is more that they can do to address their child's problem. What we do for people

Too often we underestimate the power of a touch, a smile, a kind word, a listening ear, an honest compliment, or the smallest act of caring, all of which have the potential to turn a life around.

Leo Buscaglia

with diabetes, be they adults or children, is work with the energy with a view to reducing a number of the symptoms. Patients with poor circulation due to diabetes start to notice all that changing; likewise people whose kidneys are affected will also see a difference. It is all about understanding the implications of medication and doing something about it. The ideal way to go about this is to have work carried out on the energy system in conjunction with taking the medication. As a result, people will not run the risk of encountering renal failure, ulcerations or gangrene at some stage down the road. It is important to state that we do not take people off their medication. We allow them to undergo the treatment while continuing on the medication prescribed by their GP. When a person commences the energy work, be it with or without the assistance of medical treatment, the fact of the matter is that the symptoms will not remain as severe.

When I look back on my own childhood, my main memories are that of being carefree and happy. My siblings and I were never bored and if we were caught sulking at any point, we were quickly reminded that we had nothing to be miserable about and everything to be grateful for. For some children, however, just 'being happy' in itself appears to be a challenge. Antidepressants are being prescribed to children at ages that are worryingly young. As I already stated in the last chapter, you cannot chemically analyse an emotion. So why then do parents assume that they can make their children happy by medicating them? It almost turns children into zombies as their ability to function and to be creative is distorted.

Teenagers meanwhile are under enormous stress with exams and school. I thank God I am not a teenager in today's schooling system. Despite some small efforts to tinker with the system, there is still huge pressure on both primary school children and second level students to be academically brilliant. As I mentioned in an earlier chapter the focus of the Irish education system is firmly on academia and does not sufficiently allow for our youth to develop their creativity, skills, emotions and understanding of life. Some may argue that this should be done at home. However, look at the amount of time the children are spending at school and then combine it with the amount of time their parents spend working. It is just not possible to rely entirely on such important life lessons being taught at home. School and in particular early learning should primarily concentrate on creativity. This is why I believe the whole education system needs to be revised. If the modifications could be made to incorporate more creativity, then it could provide an immense outlet for many children with problems.

Again, due care and attention must be taken at birth, and based on what I see in my clinic, this is not happening. A pregnant woman must realise that what she is carrying is a life inside her; a life that is developing and absorbing everything in her environment from what she is thinking and feeling. Motherly care should really begin at the point of conception. Rather than just looking at scans and medical tests, a whole new education has to be delivered to expectant mothers with regard to their lifestyles. They need to realise just how the nine months before the birth can hugely influence the child's development. To give

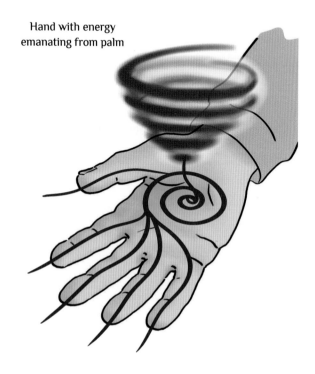

Hand with energy emanating from palm

the child the best possible start in life, expectant mothers should look into having energy treatment carried out. While undergoing the bio-energy treatment, the woman can maximise the effects by playing Mozart music, relaxing and talking internally to the child in the womb. Talking to the child is pivotal as the foetus will pick up on the vibration. In fact, the best thing an expectant mother can do is place her hand on her abdominal area, be aware of the child's breathing, its heart pumping, its lungs developing, seeing the child in her own mind and taking the time to nurture the growth of that child. Shifting the consciousness and connecting in that way can have an enormous effect on the child's ability to be placid and to relax.

What I want parents to realise is that there is hope. I want them to take from this chapter the understanding that by working with the energy system of the child, it can have a huge benefit on children with a variety of conditions. These can include ADHD, autism, dyslexia, dyspraxia, asthma, eczema, digestive disorders, rheumatoid arthritis, diabetes, to name but a few. I know this to be absolutely true because we have experienced so much success in this area in all our years treating both children and adults. Only recently, I was talking to a woman whose mother had once brought her to see us at a clinic in Dublin. She was just nine years of age at the time and was suffering from asthma. She is now twenty-nine and has never had to come back to us after that one treatment session. I assure you there are so many other people out there like that young woman; people whose lives would be dramatically different today had they not undergone the bio-energy treatment.

As a parent, you need to exhaust every avenue in order to enable your child to have the best quality of life possible. Do not depend solely on the health service and drug companies. Remember there are other ways to enhance your child's health.

REMEMBER

Love is the basis to all healing, and there is no greater love than the love a parent has for their child.

Testimony of Jackie Flynn

Clare woman, Jackie Flynn, first brought her son Adam for treatment when he was just under a year old. Many months of various antibiotics had reflected no improvement in his condition, which involved chest pains, severe wheezing and coughing. Seeing this lack of progress prompted Jackie to seek out a number of alternative options, one of which was Plexus Bio-Energy. Here Jackie gives an account of the change in Adam before the work on his energy system.

'My son's asthma problem is now cured thanks to Michael O'Doherty.'

'The whole area of bio-energy treatment first came to our attention after it was recommended to us by a friend,' Jackie recalls. 'At the time our baby boy Adam was suffering from a recurring chest infection and had been on antibiotics since he was just three months old. In fact, by the time he was a year old, he had been through eleven antibiotics and was on steroids, which was quite a lot for a child that young. Personally, I always found that the antibiotics never really cleared his chest pains, they only seemed to mask the problem.

'As Adam was so young when he first began experiencing chest pains, the doctors couldn't really determine whether he was suffering from bronchitis, baby wheeze or asthma. Overall, the general consensus was that he would grow out of it. Eventually however, it got to the point where we had to put him on a nebuliser twice a day. At night, he was unsettled and couldn't sleep

Adam Flynn

properly because he was constantly coughing due to the build-up of mucus and phlegm in his chest. I remember whenever I placed my hand on his back I could actually feel him wheezing. The medication didn't appear to be working and he was even hospitalised on two occasions with chest pains. Doctors decided then to place him on steroids in a bid to try and help clear his chest. While they might have helped the problem slightly, again I felt they weren't actually treating the condition, they were just masking it.'

Jackie recalls the change in Adam after the work done on his energy system.

'I didn't personally know Michael O'Doherty prior to Adam's treatment in his clinic,' she admits, 'so at the beginning I was sceptical. When I saw him working on Adam and waving his hands around him, I actually thought the whole thing was a bit ridiculous. However, we were at a stage where we didn't want Adam taking so many antibiotics, so we were more than willing to try alternative routes like bio-energy, as the medical route clearly wasn't working.

'Sure enough, after Adam's third treatment session with Michael, we could see a visible improvement. As well as administering the treatment, Michael made small changes to Adam's diet and it all seemed to have a positive effect on him. He is now two-and-a-half years old and I can honestly say he has never had a chest infection since undergoing the treatment.

'There was one occasion where he was taking antibiotics for his ear, but at no point since the treatment has he been on medication for his chest. Adam literally went from being on a different antibiotic every month to being on no antibiotics at all. When I look back on how bad his chest condition used to be, I very firmly believe he would be a lot worse today had we not brought him for bio-energy treatment when we did.

'Half the time Michael didn't even charge me, so it wasn't like he was telling me to bring Adam back for more treatment because he was trying to make more money from it. He was doing it because he genuinely cared for the child.'

Finally, Jackie offers advice to parents in a similar situation.

'My advice to other parents who are in a situation similar to the one I was in is to look at the alternative options. There's no harm in finding out what else is out there. As I said before, I was very sceptical at the beginning, but now I would actually advise parents to try the bio-energy treatment before they go down the medical route. There is no point placing your child on medication if there is another way their condition can be treated. To buy a nebuliser is quite costly and that's before you even take into consideration the cost of the various medications.

'As I have personally witnessed the results of the treatment through Adam, I honestly wouldn't hesitate in recommending the energy treatment to other parents.'

❧ 7 ❧

Cancer

The scourge of cancer has brought so much pain to so many people. Proof of this is that everyone knows someone whose family has been affected by it. Every week my clinic is contacted by people suffering from cancer, desperately looking to find some way to help their situation. The fact is cancer does not have to induce the fear and pain that people allow it to do. Technically, your body does not know the difference between cancer and the common cold. It is your prior knowledge, perception and reaction to the diagnosis that causes the most stress. If a doctor tells you that you are suffering from a cold, your reaction would not be one of fear. Instead, you would automatically assume that you would be able to overcome the condition. It simply would not cause you worry. If, on the other hand, you were told you had cancer, chances are you would assume the worst. Without realising it, you are allowing the fear to consume your energy.

One of the big problems at the moment is the massive increase in various forms of cancer. For people whose family members have had cancer, there is always that ever-present fear that they too may end up developing the disease. We had a classic case of this recently with a lovely lady called Hilary O'Carroll whose testimony you will read at the end of this chapter. Hilary had seen both her aunt and sister die from the disease and, consequently, was terrified that she too would one day be diagnosed with cancer. If, like Hilary, you live in an environment where you are witnessing loved ones dying from terminal illnesses, then it is the equivalent of swimming around in a pool of negative emotion waiting for the inevitable. When you see cancer taking the life of a family member, the possible genetic aspect of the disease will make you fearful that you too are at risk of developing it. That fear is then compounded by your experience with your family member's illness. This becomes your reality and because fear feeds on this reality, eventually it is possible that it too will materialise and manifest in the development of a serious problem.

The real difficulty arises in the perception the individual has of the disease when they are diagnosed with cancer. This is not helped if the person goes to their oncologist or specialist and is told that their condition is now incurable. Certainly in years gone by and sometimes nowadays, they might be told they should go home and sort out their affairs. Even though there is nothing that can be done, they might still give chemotherapy to the person in the belief that it will relieve their symptoms. They subject people to medication that can sometimes lead to more serious problems.

From a medical perspective, I believe that we are losing the battle as far as treating cancer is concerned. Multinational drug companies are not interested in discovering or creating a form of chemotherapy that will cure cancer completely. They simply have no incentive to do so as sickness is a big money-making business for them. There are huge profits to be made. When you exist in a monetary system such as this, there will be corruption from the top down. Everything works on profit. From our perspective, there is a huge need for the medical field to come forward and be honest.

When you take people who are living with someone who has cancer or who excessively fears for some reason that they may fall ill with cancer, then I believe it is inevitable that they will create the cancer. When they create the cancer, they fall into the exact same trap – the fear. They go down the chemotherapy route knowing that it probably will not solve the problem; however, they feel it is their only way to grasp onto life. Sometimes people who develop cancer are given very little or no support or advice in confronting the emotional aspect of their condition. They are told they have cancer and are then given details regarding the symptoms that accompany the cancer and the treatment on offer for it. More should be done to help people cope with the emotional effects of cancer.

When you look at the technological advances that have come about in recent times, it is very sad to think that the medical field cannot understand what exactly is causing cancer and how they can cure it. I believe the evidence is there that the cause of cancer is the breakdown within the energy structure of the body. If we dissect and analyse the part of the body that has a condition, such as breast cancer, bowel cancer or ovarian cancer, etc., what we find is an energetic frequency. We have to begin to see disease as a rogue frequency and it is possible that our technology is contributing to some of these cancers. In my opinion, in the future we are going to see an epidemic of cancers in young people, particularly those whose immune systems are compromised from the excessive use of mobile phones, from phone masts, computers, high voltage cables, etc.

There is substantial evidence based on the European-wide REFLEX study in 2004 that the radio waves from mobile phones contribute to chromosome damage. Yet despite their findings, the report stated it did not believe mobile phones posed a threat to human health. I find this conclusion unacceptable and believe that even more research is needed. Excessive use of a mobile phone during pregnancy can lead to a woman giving birth to a child with a deformity. I believe it also contributes to some cancers. To suggest therefore that the causes of cancer are unknown is just ludicrous. We already know that smoking causes 30 per cent of cancers, and radon gas is responsible for a considerable amount also. In fact, it is absolutely pointless undergoing chemotherapy to treat lung cancer if the person in question continues to smoke or is returning to an environment that contains the radon gas responsible for causing the disease in the first place.

Factors relating to cancer

Every family has been affected in one way or another by cancer, as I already stated, and yet we still remain nowhere near finding a cure. Are we any closer to a cure than we were twenty years ago? Most definitely not. In fact, if the National Cancer Registry Ireland projections are anything to go by, then the condition is projected to increase annually by a minimum of 7 per cent, and the number is set to double within the next twenty years. They have also predicted that one in three people will be diagnosed with some form of cancer. So, from what I can see, unless a major reversal of trends occurs in the near future, the number of cancer patients is likely to soar in the next twenty years beyond what is projected.

There may be little that people can do about genetic or hereditary factors when it comes to preventing cancer, but there is much they can do in relation to smoking, poor diet and alcohol, radon gas and mobile phone usage. In September 2009, I read in the *Irish Examiner* that 40 per cent of breast cancers are fully preventable by diet.

Smoking

It is well established that cigarette smoking is associated with lung cancers, but people may be unaware of the considerable proportion of cancers of the bladder, mouth and throat, stomach and pancreas also linked to smoking. In fact, smoking-related illnesses place a huge burden on the health budget. At a very conservative estimate, a minimum of €1bn of public money per year is spent on managing the health effects of smoking. Even though the evidence is there to show that smoking causes 30 per cent of all cancers (including over 90 per cent of all lung cancers), with approximately 6,000 people dying from smoking-related illnesses each year, would you believe that the number of smokers actually increased from 27 per cent in 2002 to 29 per cent in 2007? Smoking costs the economy between €1m and €5 million per day in lost productivity in the workplace. The tobacco tax level for cigarettes in Ireland in 2008 was 61.03 per cent. Therefore, for every pack of twenty cigarettes, which cost on average €7.40, the duty and VAT that went to the State was €4.51. The Exchequer receives approximately €1.19bn annually from tobacco sales.

All of the above does not make for happy reading, but I think the time has come for the Irish Government to take a serious look at this situation. I hear them talking about centres of excellence, generic drugs and the costs of providing an effective healthcare service. In fact, I put little trust in the healthcare system in light of the recent cases in misdiagnosis that has seen an increase in legal cases taken against the State for medical negligence. Unfortunately, they are failing to deal with the real issue. When you look at the cost imposed on the taxpayer to treat lung cancer and other smoking-related problems, you will see it is time for the Government to take a different approach and to force the cigarette companies to contribute financially to the treatment and caring of all patients who suffer from smoking-related problems.

Spending money trying to control cancer problems will not resolve the problem completely, however. The real issue revolves around educating society in ways that will prevent these diseases from developing in the first place. The Government invests so much time talking to doctors and consultants in an attempt to put a strategy in place. Yet when do they take the time to talk to the people of Ireland and educate them about the role they must play in preventing this serious disease from becoming an epidemic? I believe the State's efforts at health promotion to date are not sufficient. Granted there have been some advances, such as providing support to people who do wish to quit, for example, the National Smokers' Quitline. But we must make smokers and tobacco companies more responsible. The Government should force tobacco companies to pay for programmes to help get people to quit cigarettes. This approach will help to reduce the 30 per cent of cancers caused by smoking. People also need to realise that if they do not take responsibility for their own lives and health, they will end up becoming a statistic. If we are to truly conquer this problem, then what we will need are far more comprehensive and streamlined support services across the country.

Bad diet and alcohol

A bad diet without doubt contributes to cancer. Obesity and alcohol consumption are risk factors for a variety of cancers and other conditions. It is estimated that diet and tobacco together account for about two out of three cancers. That said, the Government and medical profession have consistently failed to impose the importance of eating healthy on the society they serve. In my opinion, this understanding needs to become part of our education system. If we get into the schools and provide the proper healthcare education in a systematic way, we can avoid many problems down the road. Admittedly, there has been some progress with schools such as prohibiting students from eating certain foods like sweets and fizzy drinks at lunchtime and banning sweet vending machines on their premises.

When it comes to diet and nutrition, there are a number of tips you should bear in mind. First, you should make a point of filling your daily diet with a variety of vegetables and fruit. Pay particular attention to high-fibre foods such as whole-grained cereals, legumes, vegetables and fruit. These are absolutely vital to your health. Maintain a healthy body weight and cut down on your intake of fats such as sweets, biscuits, cakes, etc. Limit your consumption of alcohol and preserved foods and, needless to say, do not undo all your good work by smoking. Set aside time each day for exercise and above all take the time to relax and enjoy your own company. Even if it is just for a half-hour each day, it will be enough to help you deal with any stress, which as we know is the biggest killer of all.

We need to place the responsibility of our nation's health with the people themselves. It is time for the Government to educate the people and not waste time, effort and money in a failed healthcare system. The key to achieving these savings is devising a healthcare plan that financially rewards healthy behaviour. Clearly, I am not the only one thinking along these lines. When I was in New York early in 2009, I heard one of the directors of the Safeway Stores discuss on TV their company's behaviour incentive philosophy and how effective it had turned out over the previous four years. He expressed the belief that well-designed healthcare reform, which utilised market-based solutions, could ultimately reduce the nation's healthcare bill by 40 per cent. The key to achieving these savings is healthcare plans that reward healthy behaviour financially. The same individual pointed out that we would be building a culture of health and fitness and, what's more, he was absolutely right. The numbers speak for themselves. Safeway's obesity and smoking rates are roughly 70 per cent of the national average in the US. So perhaps it is time the Irish Government and employers looked at a different approach? One that will encourage and motivate people to create for themselves an improved standard of lifestyle and, consequently, a better quality of heath.

There is no big secret as to why people are ill and cancer is on the increase. If we as a people refuse to change our behaviour with regard to our health, then we will have before us a very bleak future. To the multinational drug companies, it is all just a business. Do not wait until you are ill to realise the truth. Take out the yoga mat or the salad bowl; invest in your health, not in your illness.

Radon gas

A European study of radon gas, published in the *British Medical Journal* in 2004 and funded by Cancer Research UK and the European Union, discovered that domestic exposure to radon gas was responsible for a large number of lung cancer deaths. The study, the largest of its kind ever, concluded that radon gas in the home was resulting in approximately 20,000 lung cancer deaths in the European Union each year. This colourless, odourless, radioactive gas is found at varying levels in all houses across Europe and can cause lung cancer in lifelong non-smokers. Even though the risk is deemed low, it is still ever present. Smokers, on the other hand, for any given level of exposure to radon, have about twenty-five times the risk of developing lung cancer than non-smokers. This is because when radon decays it forms particles that are damaging to the cells that line the lung airways. This damage can lead to cancer and, given the lungs of smokers may already have many damaged cells, the risks of radon gas are much higher. Prof Sarah Darby of Oxford University, who spearheaded the study, pointed out that radon which had accumulated in households was still causing about 1,000 deaths each year.

Many people are either ignorant or fearful of radon gas. However, it can be relatively safe if it is not trapped in houses. Radon gas is basically formed when uranium, found in ordinary surface rocks and in soil, disintegrates naturally. The radon that circulates in the air usually disperses quickly. However, it can accumulate indoors, especially in small buildings such as houses. Even so, it is possible to reduce high radon levels in existing houses by changing the ventilation system, such as improving under floor airbricks and extracting radon from beneath the building with a fan. I would recommend that people take steps to check for excess levels of radon accumulating in their homes. By contacting the

Department of the Environment, you can get the relevant information and the relevant equipment to have your homes checked if you are concerned.

Mobile phones

In recent years, a Joint Oireachtas Committee was set up by the Irish Government to investigate the possible links between cancers and electromagnetic radiation, mobile phones and microwave radiation. Their findings concluded that there are people in our society who are electro-sensitive. Following from that, they made several recommendations to the Irish Government, which have yet to be implemented. The reason for the lack of action, I believe, stems from the fact that the Irish Government are the biggest beneficiaries of the mobile phone industry. In a report presented to the Joint Oireachtas Committee in 2005 by Dr Elizabeth Cullen on behalf of the Irish Doctors' Environmental Association, she voiced two main concerns. First, that the current 'safe' levels of electromagnetic radiation were too high and, secondly, that there appeared to be a small subgroup of the population who were unduly sensitive to that type of radiation and who needed special attention.

Dr Cullen addressed the subject of radiation and the side-effects of long-term mobile phone use. She stated that recent statistical evidence had been found to show that long-term users of mobile phones could suffer from headaches, extreme irritation, increased carelessness, forgetfulness, decreased reflexes, and clicking sounds in the ears. In addition, she noted there was statistical evidence of a significant difference in alpha and beta EEG [brain] waves on exposure to mobile phone electromagnetic field emissions positioned behind the head. In regard to the link between brain tumours and mobile phones, Dr Cullen added:

> *In studies of a possible association between brain tumours and mobile phone use, the average period mobile phones use was short compared to the known latency period of brain tumours. Although these studies did not establish an overall increased risk of brain tumours associated with mobile phone use, there were some indications of an association. Immediate effects associated with mobile phone use have been observed in human experimental studies that cannot be explained by conventional thermal mechanisms. The observed effects are within the normal physiological range and are therefore hard to interpret with respect to an increased risk to health. However, it can be concluded that mechanisms*

other than the established thermal mechanisms exist. Because of the present fragmentary scientific database, the report concluded that a precautionary approach should be adopted when dealing with radio and microwave frequency radiation for the individual and the general population.

Dr Cullen made reference to the 2004 EU report called REFLEX (risk evaluation of potential environmental hazards from low frequency electromagnetic field exposure using sensitive in vitro methods). The study involved twelve European institutes over a four-year period. It found that cells exposed to electromagnetic radiation showed a significant increase in DNA damage that could not always be repaired by the cell. This damage was also seen in future generations of cells. This effect appeared to be more noticeable in older people who took part in the study. She noted there was also evidence of damage to chromosomes, alterations in gene activity and an increased rate of cell division. The report concluded that more research was needed on animals and human volunteers.

The issue of side-effects experienced by individuals living in the vicinity of a mobile phone mast was also addressed by Dr Cullen:

There is a growing and consistent body of literature which demonstrates that a subgroup of the population appear to suffer distressing symptoms when exposed to this type of radiation. A recent survey found that people living in the vicinity of base stations reported various complaints mostly of the circulatory system, but also of sleep disturbances, irritability, depression, blurred vision, concentration difficulties, nausea, lack of appetite, headache and vertigo. This association was observed in both groups of persons who linked their complaints with the presence of the base station and those who did not. The report of the UK Independent Expert Review Group found that 'there can be indirect adverse effects on their [people living near mobile phone masts] well-being in some cases'.

In relation to the dangers of children using mobile phones, Dr Cullen made reference to the Stewart report in 2000 by the UK Independent Expert Group on Mobile Phones. This report stated that if there were currently unrecognised adverse health effects from the use of mobile phones, children may be more vulnerable because of their developing nervous system, the greater absorption of energy in the tissues of the head and a longer lifetime of exposure. The report therefore recommended that: (1) particular attention should be paid initially to the auditing of base stations near to schools and other sensitive sites; (2) in keeping with the precautionary approach, the widespread use of mobile phones by children for non-essential calls should be discouraged; and (3) the mobile phone industry should stop promoting the use of mobile phones by children.

It is no surprise that the mobile phone industry will always argue and maintain that there is no scientific evidence of harmful effects from electromagnetic radiation. The Government too is doing little by not adopting a precautionary approach. Another study, published in 2007 in the international peer-reviewed journal *Occupational and Environmental Medicine*, revealed findings that showed that a person who uses a mobile phone for more than ten years has an increased risk of developing brain cancer. The study found that those who had been using a mobile phone for a decade or more were twice as likely to develop a malignant tumour on the side of the brain where they hold the handset. Two of the scientists involved in the study, Prof Lennart Hardell of the University Hospital in Örebro and Prof Kjell Hansson Mild of the Swedish National Institute for Working Life, concluded that caution was required in the use of mobile phones. They also pointed out that children should be discouraged from using mobile phones as their delicate skulls and developing nervous systems leaves them particularly vulnerable to the consequences.

As some cancers take at least ten years or more to develop, the scientists set about assessing the risk by including in their research people who had been exposed to mobile phone radiation long enough to get the disease. They also pulled together the results of eleven studies that investigated the occurrence of tumours in people who have used phones for more than a decade. In doing so, they extracted research details from Sweden, Denmark, Finland, Japan, Germany, the United States and Britain to assemble the findings of the studies with the purpose of analysing them collectively. According to the scientists, the use of either a mobile or cordless phone for just 2,000 hours – which is less than an hour every working day for ten years – is enough to increase a person's risk of developing brain tumours.

To combat the risk somewhat, the scientists recommended buying phones that emit as little radiation as possible, particularly considering that people are being exposed to several other sources of radiation, such as WI-FI systems and masts. One of the scientists involved, Prof Mild, agreed that further research was necessary. He did add that a possible link between mobile phones and Alzheimer's disease should also be examined, especially since their study revealed indications that it might be a problem. They also stated at the time that a possible link with Parkinson's disease could not be ruled out.

I have been giving lectures in this field to several groups who are seeking answers regarding cancer clusters in the areas in which they live. Also, people who live near base stations present at my clinic believe that their symptoms of illness are associated with these appliances. I have no doubt that there is some link and I would urge the Government to take the advice of their own committee and apply the precautionary principle.

An integrated approach

We already know that electromagnetic radiation has the ability to alter the electrical activity in the cells and can manifest in cancerous conditions. I believe the cure for cancer lies in understanding how it is caused and educating people on how to confront it. By no means am I advocating that patients stop taking chemotherapy. Chemotherapy or other medical treatments may indeed help in some way, but it will not cure the disease as such. I believe an integrated approach where doctors and bio-energy therapists can work together serves everyone well in the long run.

To cure cancer, we in the clinic take an integrated approach. After working with the body at an energy level, we then look at the mindset of the patient. As part of this, we create the reality for the patient that they will return to full health. They are now taking control and focusing on their future. They are envisioning themselves perfectly healthy. We then give them techniques they can use to connect with the affected part of their body and influence what is happening in that particular part. This can be carried out by the patient through meditation or simply by them leaving their hands on the part of the body in question and imagining the healing energy pouring from the heart to the specific area. The heart energy is the energy that balances all other organs of the body. This heart area is regarded as the sacred area of our being and is the seat of divine love. If we connect to this energy of the heart, the rest of the body will react and healing will take place. Love of yourself is the basis for your healing.

We also teach the patient emotional transformation techniques to help them transform the fear into something more positive. Fear is the real killer, not the cancer. The fear feeds the cancer. What we do is teach people to realise that when the fear arises, they immediately disrupt the thought and feeling and begin practising the techniques that transforms the fear. We all experience fear, but what we must do when the fear does arise is to remind ourselves that we do not need to feel fearful; we do not need to experience it. By doing this, you are transforming the fear and connecting once again to the focus and vision of yourself of being perfectly healthy.

Once we get the energy system right and then work on the patient's mindset and focus, we then work on correcting the patient's diet. The right diet is so essential. Whenever I discuss diet with a patient, I always ensure they realise just how important it is that they cut out sugary foods. The road to health is no place for refined sugars. Bernadette Bohan, a hugely inspirational Dublin woman who was cured of cancer twice, always emphasises the importance of juicing vegetables and filling your daily diet with greens. I wholeheartedly agree with this advice and encourage my patients to follow a similar routine.

We need to take a proactive approach to our health rather than living in fear. Instead, patients need to take all the energy they are investing in the negative and channel it towards the positive. In January 2009, an article written by four highly respected individuals – Prof Dean Ornish, Prof Rustum Roy, Dr Deepak Chopra and Dr Andrew Weil – and published in the *Wall Street Journal*, confirmed the information I have already detailed in this chapter. That this new and alternative way of approaching illness is becoming more and more the preferred method of choice. A section of the article which caught my interest read:

> *The latest scientific studies show that our bodies have a remarkable capacity to begin healing, and much more quickly than we had once realized, if we address the lifestyle factors that often cause these chronic diseases. These studies show that integrative medicine can make a powerful difference in our health and well-being, how quickly these changes may occur, and how dynamic these mechanisms can be.*

> *Many people tend to think of breakthroughs in medicine as a new drug, laser or high-tech surgical procedure. They often have a hard time believing that the simple choices that we make in our lifestyle – what we eat, how we respond to stress, whether or not we smoke cigarettes, how much exercise we get, and the quality of our relationships and social support – can be as powerful as drugs and surgery. In many instances, they're even more powerful.*

Referring to President Barack Obama's stance on the issue, the article noted that heart disease, diabetes, prostate cancer, breast cancer and obesity account for 75 per cent of healthcare costs in the US, and yet these diseases are largely preventable and even reversible by changing diet and lifestyle. The article quotes President Obama when he unveiled his health plan during his campaign: 'This nation is facing a true epidemic of chronic disease. An increasing number of Americans are suffering and dying needlessly from diseases such as obesity, diabetes, heart disease, asthma and HIV/AIDS, all of which can be delayed in onset if not prevented entirely.' The above words support what I have been saying all along for the last twenty years. Disease is needless. A healthy life is within reach if you follow certain guidelines.

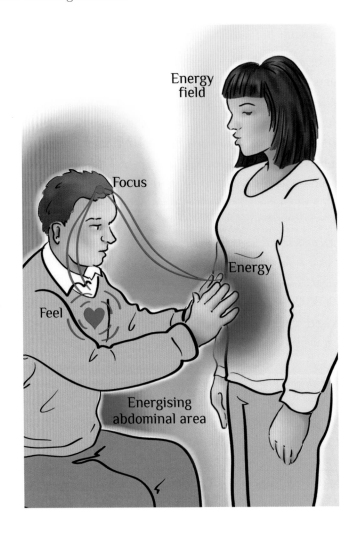

Other treatment options

Photodynamic therapy

There are many ways to treat cancer such as surgery, chemotherapy, radiotherapy, hormone therapy and biological therapies. Other beneficial treatments, however, may not have come to people's attention. For example, photodynamic therapy (PDT) has been medically proven to cure certain cancers. Although first used in the early 1900s, PDT in the modern sense is still a fairly new, evolving science. Initially, it was shown to cure skin cancer, however it has since been proven to cure other forms of cancer. It is also currently used in a number of medical fields including dermatology and cosmetic surgery. PDT is basically a medical treatment that uses a photosensitising drug – a drug that becomes activated by light exposure – such as chlorophyll, which we get from green vegetables. A laser light source is then used to activate the applied drug. The result is an activated oxygen molecule that can destroy nearby cells. Precancerous cells and certain types of cancer cells can be effectively treated this way. One of the many advantages to the treatment is that there are few side-effects. Some people are very sensitive to light and cannot tolerate the treatment, but it does not cause hair loss or alter skin colour. The procedure itself can be performed in a physician's office or in a hospital outpatient setting.

PDT essentially has three steps. First, a light-sensitising liquid, cream or intravenous drug called the photosensitiser is applied or administered. The second step concerns the incubation period of the drug. Finally, the target tissue is then exposed to a specific wavelength of light that then activates the photosensitising medication. Although the photosensitiser may be absorbed all over by many cells, atypical or cancerous cells absorb a greater amount of the drug and retain it for a longer duration than normal tissues. Tumours or atypical growths must be close to the surface of the skin or treatment surface in order for the PDT to work.

Electrochemical treatment

One of the great pioneers of medicine, Prof Björn Nordenström discovered that the body possesses its own independent electrical system. Dr Nordenström, a radiology specialist and pioneer of needle biopsy, produced a groundbreaking book in 1983 called *Biologically Closed Electrical Circuits: Clinical, Experimental and Theoretical Evidence for an Additional Circulatory System*. His thesis is that the body contains a complex electrical system that regulates the activity of the internal organs and is the foundation of health. Over the years he has treated tumours and various forms of cancers successfully with specially devised electrical probes. To treat the cancers, he inserted electrodes into the body, which in turn altered the bio-electrical activity of the cell which yielded successful results. Prof Nordenström went on to demonstrate how specific DC micro-currents, which could restore ion electricity balance, could be utilised to treat metastatic lung cancer and other malignancies successfully. His discoveries have since been replicated by many other professionals in the field. Prof Nordenström, a previous member of the Nobel Prize Committee in Medicine and Physics, was awarded the International Scientific and Technological Cooperation Award by the People's Republic of China in 2002 for his work on tumour regression. Why these treatments are not available in our hospitals is beyond me. I believe the medical profession is failing in their duty of care to provide the therapy that has been proven to heal serious disease. More so, people should demand this treatment based on the evidence provided in this book.

Take the first step in faith. You don't have to see the whole staircase, just take the first step.

Martin Luther King, Jnr

From my perspective, I would like people to be aware that these treatments exist among several others. There are many options available to people. However, the most important issue is how people confront their situation. Regardless of which treatment you choose in the end, if you believe the disease will kill you, then that is likely to be the outcome. If, however, you see yourself emerging from this as a perfectly healthy able-bodied person, then your future will be a far more positive one.

'Healing from Inside Out'

Recently I had the opportunity to watch a remarkable DVD entitled *Cancer: Healing from Inside Out*. Created by an American documentary maker Mike Anderson, the DVD involved the participation of a number of well-established figures from both the medical and alternative therapy fields, all of whom discussed chemotherapy, the consequences of undergoing this treatment, and other options available to patients. Mike's in-depth investigation into the cancer industry and the treatment it offered its patients was prompted after he lost his father to the skin cancer, melanoma. His findings, particularly with regard to chemotherapy, support everything I have written in this book. I do not know Mike personally nor have I ever met him. However, after watching his DVD I have nothing but admiration for the man. He too has seen the other side of the cancer industry and recognises the need for a different approach towards illness.

The first part of Mike's DVD concentrates on how over the past one hundred years the medical profession has worked to prevent individuals offering alternative therapies, sometimes even putting them out of business. Cutting down on such competition in the field allowed the medical profession the ideal business opportunity to create a standardised approach to treatments for various medical conditions. Doctors who dared to digress from the system or advise patients on treatments that were not part of the standardised process risked not only losing their licenses but also a jail sentence.

The second part of Mike's DVD focuses on the healing and prevention of disease through various means, some of which have already been addressed in this book. Every year thousands of people eliminate their bodies of cancer by seeking treatments outside the conventional system. What Mike found during his investigation into the American system was that the search for a cancer cure was 'hardly the altruistic endeavour you have been led to believe'. He found that, if anything, it was quite the opposite. Even worse, when statistics were examined regarding survival rate, Mike discovered that America's current cancer treatments were appallingly ineffective. One of the main treatments is of course chemotherapy.

> *What you see from studies carried out over the last fifty years is that for our major cancers, the effectiveness of conventional treatments is far less than a sugar pill. One of the problems in our approach to cancer is that it is focused on the tumour. In fact, you could say conventional medicine has a tumour fetish. The appearance of a tumour in the body is like the appearance of warning lights in your car. They appear only after the problem has developed. The medical response is to try to shrink the tumour, cut it out or start amputating body parts to get rid of it. A tumour is just a symptom of something that has gone terribly wrong inside the body. It's simply the tip of the iceberg.*

The above quotation should sound very familiar, as it is precisely what I have been saying throughout this book. The symptom is merely the warning light on the dashboard indicating the presence of a problem embedded much deeper. The only way you can truly overcome your illness is to acknowledge and treat the real problem. Chemotherapy alone cannot do this for you.

In his DVD, Mike explains how some cancer develops in our bodies over decades. He explains that the average person gets cancer cells in their body every single day of their lives. Cancer cells are circulating throughout the body at all times. In other words, he says, we all live with cancer. But the only system capable of both detecting and destroying those cancer cells is your immune system. If your immune system is impaired and a single cancer cell escapes detection, it will set up shop and start multiplying.

Most cancers, for example breast cancer, will be detected by a mammography when there are 4–10 billion cancer cells in the body. Instead of being labelled 'early detection', mammography and other similar techniques should be called 'late detection', he believes. When a tumour is detected, hospital staff try to pressure frightened patients into immediate treatment, despite the fact the some tumours have been with the patient for years sometimes decades. He later adds:

> *Most people are shocked to learn that untreated patients live as long or longer than treated patients. But then what would you expect from drugs that do great harm and give benefits no better than a sugar pill? They have not made the slightest dent on long-term survival rates. The one major cancer where mortality rates have fallen significantly is stomach cancer, however early detection and treatments had nothing to do with that. It is the declining use of food preservatives and other dietary factors that led to this decline not the treatment.*

We have all seen in some newspaper the line that 'a cure for cancer is within reach'. Unfortunately, this is anything but the case. As I have already stated in this book, illness is a big business. If the drug companies were to find a cure, they would essentially be finding a way to make less money. That is not in their interest. Think about it, when you get sick and are prescribed medication, you have to buy that medication. If you have a serious illness, the expense for the medication alone is phenomenal. If a cure were to be discovered, then what medication would you have to purchase in your quest to regain your health? Exactly! 'On the brink of a cure' and such phrases are merely bite-sized PR lines to lull us into believing that the cancer industry's massive injection of public funding is garnering results at last.

Throughout his DVD, Mike also recites a number of quotes from down through the years that, for me, really reflected how little progress our cancer industry has made with regard to treatment:

'We have given it our best effort for decades: billions of dollars of support, the best scientific talent available. It hasn't paid off.'

Dr John C Bailar, Harvard University, 1997

'For most of today's common solid cancers, the ones that cause 90% of cancer deaths each year, chemotherapy has never proven to do any good at all.'

Dr Ulrich Abel, University of Heidelberg, 1990

'…the percentage of Americans dying from cancer is about the same now as in 1970 and even in 1950…'

Fortune Magazine 2004

'…long-term survival for advanced cancer has barely budged since the 1970s.'

Fortune Magazine 2004

'Evidence has steadily accrued that cancer therapy is essentially a failure.'

Dr NJ Temple, *Journal of the Royal Society of Medicine*, 1991

'The American public is being sold a nasty bill of goods.'

Nobel Prize winner Dr James Watson, while serving on the National Cancer Advisory Board, 1975

'We are so close to a cure for cancer. We lack only the will and the kind of money that went into putting a man on the moon.'

American Cancer Society full-page ad in the *New York Times*, 1969

'Cancer deaths can be cut in half by the year 2000.'

Dr Peter Greenwald, National Cancer Institute, 1989

The last statement is certainly not what the National Cancer Registry Ireland is predicting. Dr John McDougall of Dr McDougall's Health and Medical Center, California, has been researching and promoting better nutrition for over thirty years and practising medicine for over thirty-three years. Speaking about cancer, he pointed out that despite what doctors may lead you to believe, patients actually have sufficient time to consider their next step. He explained: 'What people need to realise is that cancer is a slow growing disease and they have time to think about their next step. The problem is the doctors put them in a situation where they feel like they have to make a decision within hours. The truth of the matter is that this disease has been going on for some time before it is discovered. They should consider all the possibilities and not panic.' This is true for many patients, although for others the cancer may be causing serious and distressing symptoms that need to be treated quickly.

During the DVD, Mike made a comparison between chemotherapy and a pesticide. Just as there will always be a small percentage of insects that are resistant to any pesticide, there will always be a small percentage of cancer cells that are resistant to any combination of chemotherapy treatments. When the resistant cells survive the treatment, they reproduce and eventually return with a vengeance, just like the insects in the field. Unfortunately, many people pin all their hopes on chemotherapy as they have long been led to believe it can eliminate all cancerous cells. The reality, however, is that even a high dose of chemotherapy may not kill all the cancer cells in some patients. Mike also made a good point that if an intravenous bag spills containing a chemotherapy drug, it is deemed a major biohazard, yet here we are injecting this substance into our bodies and expecting to be cured.

A question many people voice is how does the medical profession get away with using such a perilous ineffective treatment? Some would say they are misguided. Money and good PR skills is the response I would present to such a query. Firstly, conventional medicine plays off the fact that it is seen as the only trusted method. Secondly, the sums of money involved in this business are just phenomenal. Think about it, the medical, pharmaceutical and financial industries all profit greatly from cancer treatments because such treatments are being used all the time. Dr John McDougall believes 'ego' is also a contributor to the problem. He explains:

I've been in this business for almost forty years and the same therapies
I learned forty years ago are still being used today. The same radiation,
the same surgeries, the same chemotherapy with a few additional drugs,

and the results are still the same as they were forty years ago in that the patients are getting little benefit and a lot of harm. Even though the science is absolutely clear on the limited benefits and the substantial harm of these therapies, doctor will not put a stop to them because there are the added issues of ego and the other additional factor that always dominates, which is money. This is a huge business.

There are what can only be described as astounding PR campaigns that are used by the cancer industry to re-stimulate the public's faith in their work. In 1998, there were headline articles reporting a 49 per cent decrease in the incidence of breast cancer in women who took the drug Tamoxifen for five years. As it turned out, the 49 per cent benefit is a relative number; the absolute benefit was actually only 1.5 per cent, far less than a sugar pill. If anything, Tamoxifen has many serious side-effects, just two of them being liver and uterine cancer, and as pointed out earlier can now increase the risk by four times of getting a more aggressive tumour on the healthy breast. Another example is the Herceptin drug. This drug was accompanied by reviews along the lines of 'amazing' and 'unprecedented', 'a wonder drug', and even 'a cure for breast cancer'. Drug companies claimed that clinical trials showed a 46 per cent decrease in recurring breast cancer. In fact, the absolute benefit was 1 per cent. The only thing amazing about this drug was the public relations campaign behind it.

Albert Einstein once said that the definition of insanity is doing the same thing over and over again and expecting different results. If this is true, then we as a society fit that description perfectly. We keep turning to the medical profession for treatments like chemotherapy, each time expecting them to work. Chemotherapy alone never has and never will be the solution to anyone's health problem. The sooner we realise and accept that circumstances have to change, the better chance we have of creating a promising future for both ourselves and our children.

REMEMBER

I believe the cure for cancer lies in understanding how it is caused and educating people on how to confront it.

Testimony of Hilary O'Carroll

*'"You have 15 months to live."
Now I'm cured thanks to Michael
O'Doherty.'*

'Someone once told me that chemotherapy makes Chernobyl look like a boy scout game, and they were right.' This is how Limerick woman Hilary O'Carroll sums up chemotherapy. Having experienced both sides of the system – the conventional and the natural – Hilary is one of the lucky few who can now view cancer with a greater knowledge. Her ovarian cancer was described as so aggressive that it had left her with little over a year to live, yet her oncologist still prescribed her chemotherapy even though it would have no long-term benefit. Having witnessed the disease and the treatment take the lives of both her aunt and her sister, Hilary had initially decided against chemotherapy. However, a fear instilled in her by a London oncologist saw her succumb to the treatment, all because she felt under pressure to do something immediately. She also had no knowledge of alternative treatments at that time.

While undergoing chemotherapy, Hilary researched other forms of treatment because, based on what the oncologist had said, the chemotherapy was not going to cure her cancer. Here she recounts how her will to live instilled in her the confidence and determination to seek out a different method of treatment.

'When my sister had cancer,' Hilary recalls, 'the doctors decided to give her chemotherapy and within a couple of days of receiving the treatment, her kidneys failed, her lungs collapsed and as a result, she died. What I cannot understand is why not one of the medical team asked her if she had children or siblings because it's known that when ovarian cancer occurs more than

once in a family, then the chances of the other female family members developing it increases.'

Hilary's own health began to give her cause for concern after she started to experience a persistent pain. She explains: 'Among other things, I suffered from bloating, and a persistent pain in my pelvic area and lower back. I had the symptoms of ovarian cancer but, at the time, I didn't know what the symptoms of ovarian cancer were. I just knew something was wrong. I relayed my fears to my doctor and he carried out some tests, all of which came back perfect. Even though the test results said one thing, my instinct indicated otherwise, so I pestered the doctor into carrying out further tests.

'The results of the CA125 test that came back this time showed my bloods were slightly elevated. However, the doctor pointed out that this could be as a result of something as simple as having a glass of wine too many. After hearing this, I gave up alcohol completely for six weeks. The pain however still persisted and so I was referred to an obstetrician. When I told him about the type of pain I had been experiencing and how there was a history of ovarian cancer in the family, he told me he could carry out a keyhole procedure in which he would take out my ovaries and tubes as a precautionary measure. The operation, which was scheduled for 5 December 2008, was to last no longer than forty minutes and he told me that I would be left with just a few plasters.'

The surgery, however, was not what Hilary expected. She adds: 'When I woke up that evening, the first thing I noticed was the massive bandaging. I asked why there was so much bandaging and that's when I was told the awful truth. The obstetrician explained that when he began operating on me, he was surprised by what he found. He explained I had ovarian cancer and that it had spread. At the time, I genuinely thought he had mistaken my case with that of someone else. I told him the tests that my doctor had carried out previously hadn't shown any signs of cancer, but that's when he told me that there was no one test that would detect the presence of ovarian cancer. He said he didn't know what stage my cancer was at and that he would have to refer me to an oncologist.

'I made my appointment with the oncologist and while I was waiting to see him I was given a card to take with me for a chest X-ray. I looked at the details on the card and it said my cancer was at stage three. I was shocked because my sister had died from stage four ovarian cancer. I asked the oncologist about the outcome and he said my type of cancer was extremely aggressive. He told me that I could have chemotherapy but that the cancer would return. In fact his words were: "On average patients with your condition have about eighteen months to live." He then said he would prescribe chemotherapy which might work for a few months but that the cancer would still come back and get me eventually.'

Following the diagnosis, Hilary experienced a range of emotions. Once she had accepted the news, however, she decided to seek a second opinion on her condition.

'At home afterwards, I wandered around the house numbed and in shock. I became angry because I had tried so many times to get doctors to look seriously at the pain I was experiencing. The next feeling was one of despair because it seemed that nothing could be done to help me. I wanted a second opinion. I accepted I had cancer, so I wasn't looking to find someone who would say I didn't have it, I just wanted another view on my condition.

'I went to London where my husband and I met with an oncologist. I explained to him my fears about chemotherapy. He said the only tried and tested method for cancer treatment was chemo. He then added that I would have to undergo chemo quickly because I was rapidly approaching a point where chemo wouldn't even be an option. Chemo would "buy me time" as the oncologist put it.'

Looking back, Hilary says her harrowing encounter with chemotherapy will stay with her for the rest of her life.

'Out of fear I went down the chemo route and it was a traumatic experience,' she recalls. 'The pain, nausea, fatigue, gum problems, hair loss, and the metallic taste in my mouth were only part of it. My immune system was weakened which left me prone to other infections. The irony of my situation was that while the oncologist had diagnosed a deadly cancer which he said would kill me, he also prescribed a form of treatment which, in the long term, was not guaranteeing any cure. I found myself in a desperate situation. I was extremely ill, the pain was horrendous and the vomiting was awful. I didn't have the energy to lift my head from the pillow. My energy levels were completely and utterly depleted.

'After the first week of chemo, I remember I was lying on the hospital bed in agony. They were pumping drugs into me as well as steroids but nothing eased the pain. It was just unbearable. That's when the oncologist walked over and said, "Your problem is that you have the wrong attitude".'

Despite being seriously ill at the time, Hilary managed to acquire the energy to educate herself on the other options available to her.

'Fear brought me down the chemo route, but after reading every book on cancer that I could find, I knew there were other options out there,' she explains. 'I told myself that I wasn't going to allow anyone to tell me I was going to die except God. I decided to search for my own cure because the answer to my condition did not lie in conventional medicine. Chemotherapy deals with the symptoms of cancer and not the root cause. This is why cancer recurs and people die. I read every book I could find on natural ways of dealing with cancer, particularly ovarian cancer. A clear picture soon began to emerge: cancer did not have to mean death.'

'It was important to heal, strengthen and nurture the mind, body and soul, all of which would help my body to heal itself. I had to learn to love myself and to give myself the quality time I would give to a friend in need.'

Following her research into alternative treatments, Hillary embarked on a diet and lifestyle change.

She explains: 'I changed my diet, eliminating meat and dairy. I drank plenty of fresh clean water. I took good-quality vitamin supplements and enzymes. I exercised every day. I listened to calming music and meditated, and of course I also asked God to guide and to help me.'

Recalling how Plexus Bio-Energy first came to her attention, Hilary adds: 'I was clearing out my stuff at home when on the bookshelf I came across the book Bio-energy Healing: Therapy of the Future by Michael O'Doherty and Tom Griffin of Plexus Bio-Energy. I had obviously bought it years ago but had never got around to reading it. The main idea is based on the body's natural ability to heal itself and when I read it, it was like the penny finally dropped. I knew it would help in my battle against cancer. Outside of that, I had read about Michael Flatley's story and how he had been healed by Michael O'Doherty. So I made an appointment to see Michael in his clinic.'

Several energy sessions later, Hilary began to notice a shift in her energy as well as a shift in her mindset.

'While Michael was balancing my energy, I visualised a warm healing light spreading throughout my body and melting the cancer tumours. After the first energy session with Michael, I immediately began to feel a shift in myself. I had been battling with depression and various overwhelming feelings. You begin to think things like "I've been given eighteen months to live and six have already passed", but after I left Michael's clinic, I felt like a bolt of lightning had gone through my system. I could feel a change had just taken place and I suddenly felt fantastic. I was convinced I was doing the right thing for me. At the time, I was feeling incredibly fragile because of the cancer but every time I went for an energy session, I would leave the clinic feeling cleansed and I knew it was helping my body deal with the cancer. My husband is a sceptic in the extreme but even he noticed the feeling of well-being in me. He could see something was working.'

Positive thinking took on a whole new dimension for Hilary.

'It's so important that you use your thoughts in a positive way,' Hilary adds. 'Thoughts and how you deal with them can have a huge impact on your health. It's like when someone gives you bad news and that thought is absorbed by your mind and you feel sick in your stomach. That thought has become a feeling, the feeling becomes a reaction, and it affects your whole system. However, Michael showed me how to convert negative thoughts into ones of a more positive nature and to focus on my health not my illness. This approach helped me to cope with my fear and anxiety about my condition and my apprehension concerning the impending results of a CT scan which I had recently undergone on the completion of my chemotherapy.'

Exactly seven months from the day of her initial diagnosis, Hilary received the results of a CT scan that showed there was no longer any trace of cancer in her body.

'Naturally, I was quite apprehensive on the day,' she recalls, 'but I also realised that no matter what the results showed, I was already a long way down a natural, healthy road to being cancer free.'

Hilary is convinced that the bio-energy therapy together with her own power of positive thinking has had a huge influence on her health.

'My journey to health still continues. I do not intend to become an ovarian cancer statistic. So far, it has been an amazing journey of enlightenment. Since becoming acquainted with bio-energy, my life has changed so much for the better. I now realise the importance of creating harmony not only within myself but also with my family, friends and surroundings. I now look forward with hope to a healthy cancer-free future.'

Testimony of Anna Correia

Given that Portuguese woman Anna Correia has faced severe forms of cancer and teetered on the cusp of death, it is no wonder that she finds it incredibly frustrating to hear people complaining about things like the weather. Despite being given just months to live, Anna shocked her doctors by overcoming the odds and successfully battling her cancers. Today she is a qualified Plexus bio-energy therapist and is in the process of introducing the treatment to her native Portugal. Here she recalls her own encounter with the disease and offers valuable advice to those who are currently in the midst of a sickness she knows only too well.

> 'In August, I went back to the doctor for another scan and this time they found absolutely no sign of the cancer. It had completely disappeared. Sometimes when a person has cancer in the lymph nodes, some scarring remains but I didn't even have that.'

'For most of 2004 I was suffering from pains so I knew deep inside that I was sick,' Anna begins. 'We had a lot of debts and my husband had gone to Africa so I was alone with five kids and to be honest I didn't have time to be sick. I had to sell my house and our small farm to try and pay off some of the debts. A lot of things were going on at the one time. For me, it wasn't the right time to allow myself to go to a hospital and get the treatment I needed. I can see now, though, that I was also in great denial about my situation. It was only after I had sold the house, paid what I owed, and moved to a smaller house with my kids that I went for medical treatment. By that point, I had some money in the bank, so I knew if anything happened to me, the kids would be looked after financially. Fortunately, I could also afford to hire a woman to take care of my kids while I was in hospital.

'As it turns out, there were a lot of stones in my gallbladder and I had to have an operation in which my gallbladder was removed. Afterwards, however, the pain still persisted. In fact, I remember the pains were awful. I don't know why but I felt that my pain was not entirely because of the problems I had experienced with my gallbladder. Something was telling me it was cancer. There's always a reason for it, though. I found out in May 2005 that my husband had a girlfriend in Africa and for me that was a huge shock. I see now that if you have a shock like that to your system and you're not already in good health, then sometimes it can result in diseases like cancer.

'When they operated on me in November 2005, they discovered that I had cancer in three different places. I had it in the uterus and in both the right and left ovaries. The doctor I first visited about my illness was actually a friend of mine and I had arguments with him from July to November to do the tests and to carry out the operation. I suppose he just didn't want to believe I was sick with a disease.

'When he did perform the operation and found that I had not one but three forms of cancer, he came to my house a week later to give me the results. I remember he was crying so much. He kept saying to me "I don't know how you're alive." They then decided to perform another operation in December – a biopsy of the lymph nodes.'

While the results of the December biopsy would show that the tumours had been successfully removed from her body, unfortunately Anna's run of luck was not to last. After moving to Ireland in late 2006, her gut feeling told her the cancer was back. Test results subsequently proved her instinct right.

She recollects: 'I remember feeling really tired so I went to the doctor and gave him all my medical papers from Portugal relating to the cancers I had the year before. I told him that I thought the cancer was back, so we went through all the tests again and he did a CT scan. The results showed that the cancer had returned on the lymph node near where it had been on the right ovary. Doctors tried to carry out a biopsy but were unsuccessful, so their only other option was to put me on chemotherapy. I had to get the strongest chemotherapy because they didn't know if the cancerous cells were from the uterine cancer or the ovarian cancer. I underwent chemotherapy from August to December 2007.'

To deal with the physical pain that accompanies not just the cancer but also the chemotherapy, Anna looked into the realm of alternative treatments available.

'At one point, I was really desperate for a solution because I had pains all over my body from the chemo,' she recalls. 'They were giving me morphine *for the pain, but I was very tired most of the time. All I wanted to do was sleep, which was very difficult because I had five children to look after. I was a very busy person. I did acupuncture and Reiki for a while, but then I saw a sign for a Plexus bio-energy clinic in Mullingar, where I was living at the time. After the first four days of treatment, I underwent a programme with Tom Griffin, who was working with his partner Michael O'Doherty in Ennis. Following the treatment, I began to feel more energetic and I could actually sleep properly for the first time. At that particular point, I couldn't walk anywhere without crutches as the lymph nodes had left my legs and feet very swollen. Following the energy treatment, however, I could walk without crutches for the first time because the swelling in my feet had gone down.'*

In December 2007, Anna chose to stop her chemotherapy, a decision that was met with much opposition.

'I remember I had a lot of arguments with the doctors about it. Even Michael O'Doherty was concerned about me stopping the chemo,' Anna recalls. 'He told me I should be having the chemotherapy in conjunction with the bio-energy treatment as it would increase my chances of beating the cancer. I had already made up my mind, though, that I was stopping the chemo. I was skin and bone at the time and I knew if I continued the chemo I would die from it.

'In April 2008, I underwent another CT scan. The results of this scan left me very upset because it showed the cancer had actually grown. The doctor again asked me to go back on the chemotherapy but I was still against the idea. I continued on with my Plexus bio-energy training with Michael O'Doherty and Liam Fretwell. I also continued with my daily healing treatments.

In August, I went back to the doctor for another scan and this time they found absolutely no sign of the cancer. It had completely disappeared. Sometimes when a person has cancer in the lymph nodes, some scarring remains but I didn't even have that. Before the tests were carried out I knew deep down that the cancer was no longer there. The first time I realised, it was back in July. I can't explain it, I just knew. My energy was back and I just felt really happy. Even my family noticed a change in me at the time.'

While Anna had stood firm on her decision to stop the chemotherapy, she admits her choice did worry her. However, you will never hear Anna bemoaning the hardship her illness brought upon her. Instead, you will hear her talk optimistically about life and her appreciation for the chance she was given to live it to the full.

'Of course I had some worries about stopping the chemotherapy,' Anna says. 'When you have cancer you are always worried. The thing is, we are all going to die, but some people just don't realise this until they have an illness. In one way, I'm happy I went through the experience because I appreciate life more, and now I make time to stop and think about the way I am living. I'm a completely different person now to the one I was before the cancer. In a way, it was a blessing in disguise.

'Because of what I went through, I can relate more to people with cancer. When I treat them, I know what they are going through because I have been there myself. They open up to me and sometimes they cry. For some patients, it's the first time they have cried since they were diagnosed. They can speak with me about their fears because they know I understand. The only thing a doctor can offer is chemotherapy or radiotherapy. There is no support offered in the form of someone to talk to. When I was ill, I went to a support centre in Mullingar for people with cancer. It was there I had access to psychologists for my kids. I realised that everyone needs help and that at the time I couldn't help my kids because I was so sick. Hospitals should be offering this kind of service.'

Since developing a newfound appreciation for life, Anna justifiably does not allow time for fear or negativity.

'Cancer gave me the opportunity to realise that life was for living and not for running around in a stressful state,' she explains. 'I refuse to get caught up in the small things. I can't deal with people complaining about little things like the rain and what not. I think it's because I went through so much in my own life that it frustrates me to hear people moaning about the small things. I don't even pay attention to the economic problem.

She adds: 'I never let fear stop me from doing things now, and I certainly don't believe in putting things off either. If I don't have the courage to do a particular thing, then I just deal with the fear and then do it. I don't ignore it. I let the fear come out, I don't hide it. I ask myself why I'm afraid of something and then I deal with it. Now before I go to sleep, I always acknowledge the things I am grateful for in life.'

As a result of both her experience with Plexus bio-energy treatment and a desire to work with people, Anna decided to study with the Plexus Institute to become a qualified therapist. While she was eager to help make the treatment available to as many people as possible, Anna also found herself having to prepare for those who simply didn't want to fight any longer.

Considering that from a young age she found herself very sensitive to the different energies possessed by people, it would seem Anna was destined for the role of a Plexus bio-energy therapist. She now hopes her story will help educate people about the dangers of suppressing their emotions.

'People need to realise that something like a shock can have an affect on you, even ten years after it has happened. The shock stays in your system until you have dealt with it. Whether you suffered the trauma of an accident, the break-up of a relationship or the death of a loved one, it will result in disease if you do not deal with it.

'My husband and I are separated, but I am now in the grieving process for that separation. I need to go through the grieving process because I know if I don't, I will be sick in years to come.'

Finally, she adds: 'After the first operation I realised that I wasn't afraid of dying, I was afraid of living. Most of the people I know live like that. We don't enjoy the small moments; we don't laugh enough and we postpone far too many things. After everything I've been through, my advice to people would be to stop worrying and to start living.'

8

Your Own Personal Plan: Diet and Meditation

Diet plays a major role in one's recovery as disease often begins with poor dietary habits. One way of improving your health and well-being is through juicing. Juices are packed with nutrients and bursting with flavours. I can promise you there is no better way to recharge your batteries than with freshly extracted fruit and vegetable juices. They have outstanding nutritional qualities and begin their cleansing and healing of the body within fifteen to thirty minutes of being consumed. Compared with solid foods, juices are easily assimilated by the body. This means the workload on our digestive system is reduced, which facilitates a more efficient performance of cleansing and elimination.

Our bodies are very often overloaded and clogged up with accumulations of waste and toxins that constantly flow through the body. Green juices such as cucumber and celery are excellent spring cleaners and an easy way to detox the body. Juices overall are a perfect means to stimulate better elimination of waste and toxins and also assist with the detoxification process. I often think we are obsessed with cleaning on the outside of the body, but we tend to forget the hugely important task of cleansing out the internal organs. These cleansing drinks will flush out your system very thoroughly and, when taken first thing in the morning, will immediately inject a new lease of life into your system. They are also less expensive and far less invasive than other detox methods now available. I personally have witnessed many patients with long histories of chronic constipation and congested intestines alleviate these conditions with great success by taking these green juices. To ensure the juices were given the best possible chance to work, the patients also eliminated junk foods from their diet and drank plenty of fresh clean water.

Juices are highly concentrated forms of nutrition and are of particular value to people fighting any kind of disease. Not many people realise that as a result of their therapeutic properties and healing powers, juices are actually used in many natural healing centres throughout the world. Juices revolutionise your body's ability to heal itself as well as boosting your natural self-defences. Their benefits are quite phenomenal and the results they will bring about in your body will be noticed and felt by you. You can help your body to become a picture of health regardless of what age you are, and what better way to do so than to increase your intake of fruits and vegetables. If you are a parent, it is also highly advisable that you give your child a head start in life by increasing their intake of these delicious-tasting juices.

Including these in your diet will be one of the healthiest steps you can take for your body. With just two glasses of juice per day, you can consume large quantities of fruits and vegetables. For two 8 fl oz (240ml) glasses of juice per day, you would need six to eight portions of fruit and vegetables. To eat your way through that many pieces would take quite some time, yet here you have them all in two glasses. The point of increasing your intake is to provide your body with enough vitamins, minerals, enzymes, and trace elements to support a healthy body and give sustained energy levels. A well-hydrated body is essential for good skin and enhanced vitality. Even people with the best heath intentions find it difficult to drink large amounts of water each day, yet these delicious drinks can easily increase fluid intake. The process of eating healthily does not have to be complicated. In fact, I have repeatedly stated that the secret is to keep it simple: this way you are far more likely to succeed. You can then comfort and nourish your body with delightful scrumptious foods. As food is the body's major source of nutrients, enriching a deficient diet will immediately help optimise your health. The good foods will help you support the body's basic needs and functions as well as reversing the many symptoms of disease.

To exemplify the potential of a good diet and plenty of juicing, let me tell you about an amazing lady called Bernadette Bohan. I met her recently as part of a health programme we were giving in Grove House, a health spa in Cork. Bernadette had recovered from cancer by making far-reaching changes to her diet and lifestyle. As such, she is well placed to advise us on this subject and I believe her books *The Choice* and *The Choice: The Programme* are well worth using as part of your dietary plan for health.

Even though there is a large selection of wonderful foods on offer that are full of nourishment and vitality, many of the foods we choose to eat not only lack nourishment but also contain harmful ingredients. I have listed four groups of foods that we need to curtail.

Sugars

Sugars are needed by the body but not in the huge quantities we consume. They are one of the most addictive foods we have acquired a taste for in today's Westernised diet. Large amounts of sugars are found in cakes, muffins, biscuits, chocolate, and even in white bread and pasta. What is more, these are just a fraction of the sugar-laced foods to which we have become totally addicted. It is undoubtedly hard to accept the fact that when we eat these foods we are slowly digging our own grave. The phrase 'it was to die for' may need a bit of a rethink. Ask any parent of a child with ADHD/ADD and they will tell you that if they give them sweet foods, the child is likely to climb the walls such is the effect.

What is it that makes sugar so bad? Sugar is strong enough to penetrate tooth enamel, so you can only imagine the damage it can cause within your body. When we eat these sugary foods they are absorbed very quickly into the bloodstream and as such our bodies are pushed into a state of emergency. This may seem a bit over the top, but refined sugars have been connected to a multitude of diseases, including diabetes, cancer, arthritis, heart disease, Crohn's disease and obesity. Think about it. Sugar is a refined food and lacks all the nutrients necessary for its digestion. It simply draws from our body's stores of enzymes. If you need your fix of something sweet, then natural plant sources of sweeteners like Agave syrup (cactus plant) can be used instead of refined sugars and are available in good health stores. Some people prefer to replace their sugary fix with small amounts of honey.

Dairy foods

Yes, it is certainly true that our bones need calcium, but contrary to popular belief we do not need the calcium from cow's milk. Let me first explain that a deficiency in calcium is not the cause of osteoporosis (loss of bone mass and demineralisation). It is firstly a disease of excess proteins that increases excess acid in the body. This acid increases the excretion rates of precious calcium and leeches it from our bones. I know it may be difficult to grasp that cow's milk is not meant for human consumption when we have been conditioned to believe otherwise for so long. It is in fact no way essential to human health. Basically, the human body does not require milk after weaning, as at this stage we produce less of the lactase enzymes necessary for its digestion. Its nutrient profile is completely different to mother's milk.

Milk contains the sugar called lactose. Lactose is a disaccharide, which means it contains two different sugars bound together. For lactose to be absorbed, it must be first split into those two smaller sugars. An enzyme called lactase, which is found in the lining of the small intestine, is responsible for carrying out this split. The split does not happen if the levels of the lactase enzymes are low or absent and the person is lactose intolerant. Instead the lactose is fermented by bacteria in the large intestine, producing excess gas that can lead to bloating, pain and diarrhoea.

Milk can be responsible for sparking off and producing sensitivities and allergic reactions. Initially this may be identified as digestive upsets and diarrhoea or causing inflammation in the mucous membranes and lungs. An excess of mucous is believed to cause ear infections, runny nose and persistent sore throats. Most of us recognise if we have a negative response to specific foods, therefore, it is important to go with your instincts in these cases.

Food chemicals

Also escaping our attention is the large concentrations of chemical residues found in milk cheese and cream. Antibiotic and antiparasitic drugs when coupled with fertilisers and pesticides in the animal's food are nothing short of a chemical soup. It may be wise to consider a reduction in these dairy foods so as to reduce your exposure to these chemicals. I think it would be wise to remember that dairy products should not be viewed as an ideal source of food for you and your children. It is also worth remembering that nature did not provide these so-called nourishing foods. The dairy industry did.

Fats

Heated fats have a horrific impact on our health. When we heat fats they can turn from healing fats into killing fats. Over the past thirty years, fats have developed a very bad name, so much so that many people live on 'low fat' diets under the firm belief that fats add nothing but calories to their food. With this 'fat phobia' on the increase, it is imperative to recognise the difference between good fats and bad fats.

Traditionally, oils were mechanically cold pressed in small amounts for immediate consumption. They were distributed to local households in much the same way as the milkman brings fresh milk, as fats turned rancid rather quickly. These days we have refrigeration and chemical methods that prolong the shelf life of these oils. However, the fats we consume today are fundamentally different from what was consumed by our ancestors in the not too distant past. Industrialisation has brought about large-scale production of oils, and now huge expeller oil presses have replaced the smaller, slower, cold temperature mechanical presses of the past. Modern technologies have found new methods of processing that allow manufacturers to produce cheap, low-quality oils with a longer shelf life.

So what happens when we heat oils? When we heat fats we upset their delicate balance. The heating process alters the molecular structures of these fats producing free radicals, which are destructive molecular fragments that are formed during metabolism. Heating at high temperatures turns these oils into twisted molecules called trans-fatty acids. The heat causes the fatty acid bonds to break down creating free radicals in the form of short-chain fatty acids, trans-fats, and saturated fats. These fats are all too happy to react with oxygen and when rapid oxidation occurs, it increases the dangers to our health. These unnatural fats are toxic and can interfere with cell function and the use of oxygen in the cells.

Exposing *good fats* to heat will destroy their long-carbon chain bonds and change them to short-chain fatty acids, thus becoming trans-and-saturated fats. These heated unnatural fats leave us wide open to the increased danger of free radical damage, which may cause an array of health problems. Oils prepared in this damaging way are better known as hydrogenated or partially hydrogenated oils. This type of oil now becomes more shelf stable at room temperatures, which for commercial reasons is far more profitable. You will find hydrogenated oils and partially hydrogenated oils in bakery products, frozen foods, margarines, and many more products on the market, so check your labels.

As our health is based on the amount of absorbable nutrition we provide to our bodies, it appears to me that it is necessary to return to some grassroots solutions if we are to solve the problems left in the wake of our impoverished diets. My experience has taught me that the closer to nature we live, the more we live without disease and problems.

We see many children in our clinics and in truth many children are suffering from malnutrition. While they are not hungry or lack food, it is just the type of food they eat. Too much sugar and bad fats play a detrimental role in the child's health and development. In the supermarket, I often see people carrying trolleys of rubbish foods but what they do not realise is that they are investing money in their illness. Parents should have a look at the foods in their shopping trolleys and ask themselves if those foods possess any nutritional value. Children in my opinion must not get any sweet foods, such as biscuits, chocolates, crisps, fizzy drinks, nor too many dairy products.

Destiny is not a matter of chance, it is a matter of choice; it is not a thing to be waited for, it is a thing to be achieved.

William Jennings Bryan

It is clear to me that children lack exercise and fresh air because they spend too much time on computer games and watching TV, eating rubbish foods. Obesity in our society is becoming a big problem and putting a huge strain on our health system, yet the source of the problem lies in bad diet and lack of exercise. Again we need to link health to behaviour, and our behaviour in this case has to change. As I stated earlier in this book, educating our children regarding their health must begin in the schools.

Liam Fretwell conducting a class on the beach in Lahinch, County Clare in 2005

Meditation

There is no disputing that meditation is one of the most important elements of any healing programme. In fact, the benefits of meditating have been well established scientifically. One benefit is a reduction in stress levels. Certain groups of people have particular difficulty dealing with stress: for example, research shows that ADHD children have slower brain development and a reduced ability to cope with stress. However, the use of meditation now has proven benefits for these children. A US study from 2008, published in *Current Issues in Education,* followed a group of ten junior high school (middle school) students with ADHD who were practising the transcendental meditation technique twice a day in school. After three months, researchers found over 50 per cent reduction in stress and anxiety, as well as improvements in ADHD symptoms. The effect was much greater than the researchers had expected. The children also showed improvements in attention, working memory, organisation and behaviour regulation. In fact, after the in-school meditation routine had begun, teachers reported they were able to teach more and students were able to learn more because they were less stressed and anxious.

Everyday our bodies are exposed to stress. However, we have the capability to transform this stress in a very positive way through the process of self-awareness. Stress management is a growing practice throughout the modern world and, unfortunately, due to the lack of self-awareness, we depend on others to manage our stress for us. This brings to mind the quotation from the Bible: 'Physician heal thyself.' How true this statement is even today. We must realise that the responsibility for our health is *ours* and not that of someone else. We have to consciously learn to identify with our own lives and be responsible for our own actions and reactions. Then when we are happy, we are more content within ourselves. It is almost as though everything seems to work for us in a very positive and constructive way when in this frame of mind.

To learn the techniques of how to transform your stress into vitality is relatively simple. Nonetheless, it does require self-discipline and a willingness to participate in a self-management programme. By implementing the programme outlined below, you can transform that stress, be it emotional, mental or physical, into sheer vitality.

Personal assistance protocol

- When you wake up, make it a point to drink some warm water, which can help internal cleansing. Most people wake up dehydrated.

- Try to give some time to limber up your body, even if it means going to bed ten minutes earlier.

- Tap and rub your kidneys lightly in the morning and in the late afternoon.

- Tap and gently massage the area of your thymus gland in the early morning and throughout the day, especially when you feel illness coming on. Your thymus gland is found just behind your breastbone.

- Moderate your food intake to times when you feel hungry, as overeating drains your body's energy.

- Take time to practise abdominal breathing, as this can help to centre your awareness and thus leave you more focused.

- Take a few moments throughout the day to practise internal awareness by adopting a visualisation technique. (Remember to practise abdominal breathing for a few minutes beforehand.)

- Do not eat late at night as this can reduce your quality of sleep and thus drain your body's energies. (Sleep should heal not reduce your energy.)

- Remember to 'undress your stress' before you go to bed each night. This means renewing the practice of letting go of all of the day's stress.

The benefits of water

Considering that water is the very liquid that will keep a body in good health, I simply cannot understand why most people do not drink enough water. Our bodies have to replace about 2.2 litres of water each day. Correct hydration is therefore essential for good health.

Most people associate the old adage of 'eight glasses a day' with cosmetic benefits such as clear skin and nails. While this is all true, it is important not to forget the direct role played by water in the maintenance of good health not to mention its ability to reduce the risk of certain cancers. The functions of water are indeed wide and varied. It transports nutrients to the cells within your blood, helps you digest your food and regulates your body temperature through respiration and perspiration. It also improves your memory of recent events and helps to maintain your body weight at the correct level.

Water retention: When you fail to drink enough water, your body instead begins to retain water in order to compensate for the lack. To overcome water retention problems, you should drink more water not less. In fact, the less water you drink, the more your body sees its survival as being threatened and so conserves every drop. This results in water being stored outside the cells, which in turn causes swelling of the feet, legs and hands. The good news is that the body can get rid of the excess liquid but this is only done once the necessary water levels have been replenished. Remember fluid retention can be caused by heart and kidney conditions too, so do ask your doctor about how much fluids you should be taking in this case.

Breathing: Water is essential for you to breathe. To take in oxygen and get rid of carbon dioxide, your lungs must be moistened by water. In fact, you lose between half a litre and a litre of water each day just by breathing.

Brain: Were you aware that depression and chronic fatigue syndrome can arise from dehydration? In fact, dehydration plays a major role in causing migraines as well. Basically, your brain tissue consists of 85 per cent water and so when dehydration kicks in, your level of energy production in the brain begins to decrease.

Joints: Water is also needed to lubricate your joints. When the cartilage is properly hydrated, the surfaces are able to slide smoothly over each other, ensuring there is little damage caused by friction. If the cartilage is dehydrated, there is more damage from abrasion, resulting in the joints deteriorating further.

Back: If you suffer from back pain, it may be worth increasing your intake of water as backaches are often eased by good hydration. According to chiropractors, the volume of water stored in your spine supports 75 per cent of the weight of your body and 25 per cent of the fibrous material around the disc. Seeing that the joints in your spine depend on the hydraulic properties of the water stored in the disc, back pain could be relieved greatly by increasing your intake of water.

Kidneys: Kidney damage can also occur if you are dehydrated. The role of your kidneys is essentially to remove waste products, such as urea and lactic acid, by means of water. When there is insufficient water, however, these waste products are not removed effectively. Thus, it can lead to kidney damage.

Weight loss: When you feel hungry, your body is often only just dehydrated. Rather than going straight for the fizzy drinks, the best way to cure this dehydration is to opt for a large glass of water instead. It contains no calories and also helps to reduce your appetite and helps your body to metabolise fats.

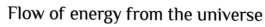

Flow of energy from the universe

Energy
field

Meditation – flow of earth energy

Physical and health benefits of meditation

As meditation gained greater prominence in Western society, scientists began to calculate its physical benefits in countless studies. Today significant benefits have been found for many health conditions, including heart disease, high cholesterol, high blood pressure, insomnia, chronic pain, cancer and immunity. The use of meditation to ease a wide variety of societal and health problems is very encouraging as it is a low-cost intervention with practically no side-effects. In the book *Freedom from Stress*, David and Karen Gamow highlight the benefits of meditation and the research to support it.

- In a study of health insurance statistics, meditators had 87 per cent fewer hospitalisations for heart disease, 55 per cent fewer for benign and malignant tumours, and 30 per cent fewer for infectious diseases. The meditators had more than 50 per cent fewer doctor visits than did non-meditators.[1]

- Meditation lowers blood pressure to levels similar to prescription drugs for those who have normal blood pressure or moderately raised. [2]

- Meditation increases circulation in novice meditators by 30 per cent, and in experienced meditators by as much as 65 per cent.[3]

- Meditation has been endorsed by the National Institutes of Health as effective for the relief of chronic pain. Chronic pain sufferers experience a reduction in symptoms of 50 per cent or more.[4]

- Seventy-five per cent of long-term insomniacs who have been trained in relaxation, meditation and simple lifestyle changes can fall asleep within twenty minutes of going to bed.[5]

- Meditation reduces blood sugar levels in diabetics.[6]

- A group of inner-city residents suffering from chronic pain, anxiety, depression, diabetes and high blood pressure were trained in meditation. They experienced a 50 per cent reduction in overall psychiatric symptoms, a 70 per cent decrease in anxiety, and a 44 per cent reduction in medical symptoms.[7]

Mental and productivity benefits of meditation

David and Karen Gamow also looked at research on meditation that showed significant improvements in mental health, memory, concentration and productivity.

- Brain scans show that meditation shifts activity in the prefrontal cortex (behind the forehead) from the right hemisphere to the left. People who have a negative disposition tend to be right prefrontal oriented. Left prefrontals have more enthusiasm, more interests, relax more and tend to be happier.[8]

- Researchers tested novice meditators on a button-pressing task requiring speed and concentration. Performance was greater at forty minutes of meditation than after a forty-minute nap.[9]

- Meditation helps chronically depressed patients and reduces their relapse rate by half.[10]

- Meditators notice more, but react more calmly than non-meditators to emotionally arousing stimuli.[11]

- Those with smoking, alcohol and eating addictions who have been trained in meditation break their addictions with significantly lower relapse rates than those receiving standard therapies.[12-15]

- Middle school children who practise meditation show improved work habits, attendance and grade point average.[16]

- Brain scans of meditators show increased thickness in regions of the cortex associated with higher functions like memory and decision making.[17]

- Meditation appears to slow ageing. Those meditating five years or more were twelve years younger than their chronological age.[18]

REMEMBER

Everyday our bodies are exposed to stress and we have the capability to transform this stress in a very positive way through the process of self-awareness.

References from *Freedom from Stress*

[1] D Orme-Johnson, *Pschosomatic Medicine* 49 (1987): 493–507.

[2] M Murphy, S Donovan, *The Physical and Psychological Effects of Meditation* (Institute of Noetic Sciences, 1997).

[3] M Murphy, S Donovan, *The Physical and Psychological Effects of Meditation* (Institute of Noetic Sciences, 1997).

[4] J Kabat-Zinn, L Lipworth, R Burney, W Sellers, 'Four year follow-up of a meditation-based program for the self-regulation of chronic pain,' *Clinical Journal of Pain* 2 (1986): 159–173.

[5] G Jacobs, *Say Goodnight to Insomnia,* (Owl Books, 1999).

[6] H Cerpa, 'The effects of clinically standarised meditation on type 2 diabetics,' *Dissertation Abstracts International* 499 (1989): 3432.

[7] B Roth, T Creaser, 'Meditation-based stress reduction: experience with a bilingual inner-city program,' *Nurse Practitioner* 22(3) (1997): 150–2, 154, 157.

[8] R Davidson, J Kabat-Zinn et al, 'Alterations in brain and immune function produced by mindfulness meditation,' *Psychosomatic Medicine* 65 (2003): 564–570.

[9] Reported in *The Boston Globe* (Nov 23, 2005).

[10] JD Teasdale, ZV Segal, JMG Williams, V Ridgeway, M Lau & J Soulsby, 'Reducing risk of recurrence of major depression using mindfulness-based cognitive therapy,' *Journal of Consulting and Clinical Psychology* 68 (2000): 615–23.

[11] M Murphy, S Donovan, *The Physical and Psychological Effects of Meditation* (Institute of Noetic Sciences, 1997).

[12] CN Alexander, P Robinson, M Rainforth, 'Treatment and prevention of drug addiction,' *Alcoholism Treatment Quarterly* 11 (1994): 11–84.

[13] J Kristeller, B Hallett, 'An exploratory study of a meditation-based intervention for binge eating disorder,' *Journal of Health Psychology* vol 4 (1999): 357–363.

[14] PA Royer-Bounouar, 'A new direction for smoking cessation programs,' *Dissertation Abstracts International* 50, 8-B (1989): 3428.

[15] M Shafii, R Lavely, R Jaffe, 'Meditation and marijuana,' *American Journal of Psychiatry* 131 (1974): 60–63.

[16] H Benson, M Wilcher et al, 'Academic performance among middle school students after exposure to a relaxation response curriculum,' *Journal of Research and Development in Education* 33(3) (2000): 156–165.

[17] Massachusetts General Hospital, reported by Carey Goldberg, *The Boston Globe* (Nov 23, 2005).

[18] RK Wallace, MC Dillbeck, E Jacobe, B Harrington, *International Journal of Neuroscience* 16 (1982): 53–58

Testimony of Matt Molloy, musician with The Chieftains

I first heard about the work of Michael O'Doherty through my friend Michael Flatly. I had been going through a particularly bad time as my beloved wife was quite ill and everything subsequently took its toll on my health.

'When I look back at how low I was feeling last year, I can see just how much I have improved in the space of twelve months.'

My energy levels were depleted, my immune system was down and overall it became quite difficult to motivate myself. So when I heard about the wonderful results experienced by Michael Flatly, I decided to look into it and see if it would work for me.

Admittedly, I was initially dubious about the process. Following the first session, however, I could feel a better sense of well-being. Maybe it's different for others, but for me it gave me the push I needed. At the time I was also experiencing problems with my hip. Following a number of treatment sessions, however, these problems completely cleared up. I just felt an amazing overall sense of well-being.

Michael and musician Matt Molloy

While the energy work itself was hugely effective, I found Michael's optimism and enthusiastic nature a wonderful help to my healing process. He is very well able to express himself and as such he motivates you to motivate yourself. When your immune system and energy levels are down, it can sometimes be very difficult to encourage yourself to get out and do things.

Michael, however, exudes such energy and reassurance that you begin to feel energised just by speaking with him. He has a great perception of people and when he outlines the process of how a person becomes ill, you find it makes so much sense. He explained the psychology very clearly to me and I completely understood what had to be done in order for my health to improve. When I look back at how low I was feeling last year, I can see just how much I have improved in the space of twelve months.

God has given Michael a gift to help people, and, from my own experience with sporting injuries, his treatment definitely works.

Gary Kelly

Michael and Gary Kelly, the former Irish Republic and Leeds United soccer player

9

The Consciousness Shift

Mickey Mantle, an American baseball player plagued with lifelong ill-health, once joked: 'If I had known I was going to live this long, I'd have taken better care of myself.' Even though the great athlete was cracking a humorous remark at the time, his words hold significant advice nonetheless. Erase any possibility of future regrets with regard to your health by taking proper care of yourself today.

The good news is that no matter what age you are, it is never too late to begin the journey towards good health and well-being. As you already know from having read the patient testimonies, no age is off limits as far as energy work is concerned. I sincerely hope you take from this book the realisation that you do not have to be ill. You do not have to be depressed; you do not have to be unhappy; things can change if you really want them to change.

As I have stated in previous chapters, sickness is a reflection of what is going on deep within ourselves. It is a natural reaction to an unnatural state of affairs. It is nature's way of attempting to draw our attention to aspects of our being that we are ignoring. Effectively, what has happened in our society is that we have become observers. We do not truly understand how we function fundamentally because we have not been educated to understand what really causes our problems, be they addictions, ailments, depression, etc. It is time we all abandoned the observation post and took up a participating role. We need to become more proactive in our lives. If it is health and happiness you are seeking, then get out there and get it, because, believe me, it is there for you if you truly want it.

Energy is the web that unites all reality, and each one of us is made up of the same stuff as the universe. However, unless you participate in creating your own reality and everything you do, then you are going to become susceptible to problems. You will become caught up in a mindset that inhibits your creative ability and you will stagnate at all levels. There is a need for people to realise that ultimately sickness is not something we should be afraid of. It is not something that should be allowed to strike fear into us. Do not give sickness the control; remember it is your body, you decide the outcome. You may feel that you do not have the ability to achieve what you would like, but all the elements of success are contained within your being and this process begins by just your imagination.

Risk! Risk anything! Care no more for the opinion of others, for those voices. Do the hardest thing on earth for you. Act for yourself. Face the truth.

Katherine Mansfield

We need to shift our consciousness and raise our awareness of who we truly are, and reconnect to the multidimensional aspect of our being. We need to understand how we function in this world of energy, how we are connected to and a part of the whole. For many years, there was a belief that disease was caused by a breakdown in the chemical structure of the body. That view no longer is valid. From now on, you have to ignore the notion that disease is incurable and that drugs and operations are your only solutions to overcoming the disease. Remember, medicine as we know has to change and incorporate what I have outlined in this book if the real cure for all disease is to be found. You have to eradicate the negative perceptions from your consciousness, because that forms your imagination and your vision of the future and will in time become your reality. Instead, change the way in which you view things. If you do not, you will simply become ill. You need to expose yourself to the understanding that your body is made up of non-physical material called energy. Even in perception terms, isn't it nicer to think you have a body filled with energy that is in continuous flow and exists in abundance all around us than one filled with chemicals?

Many eminent scientists from Björn Nordenström to Valerie Hunt to Albert Einstein and a host of other physicists and cosmologists have stated that matter, your body, is condensed energy. Our bodies are all the time physiologically inheriting information that is stored within the energy systems of our bodies. Basically, if you keep telling yourself you are sick, or that you will not get better, then your body will take that on board and make it a reality. Within that energy system is the capacity to initiate structuring and functioning of the organ systems of our body. Another example is the patient who immediately resigns themselves to the idea that death is to be their fate within the next few months, simply because a doctor told them they have just months to live. No one can tell you your time is up except for God himself. However, for some reason we give these institution

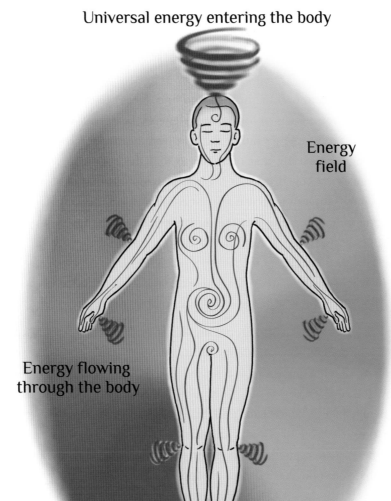

Universal energy entering the body

Energy field

Energy flowing through the body

Energy entering the body from the earth

God status, which they do not deserve. We have to shift our whole focus from ill-health to good health. We have to stop giving illness our energy and instead start focusing on channelling it towards good health. Do not waste time and energy worrying that you will be next to catch swine flu or get some other disease. Instead invest that same energy and time into believing that you will remain free of any illnesses or viruses doing the rounds.

In order for us to become healthy and find deeper understanding and meaning, then we have to focus on ourselves as energy beings. If you focus on a disease as a blockage of energy rather than a physical problem, then you can focus on removing or releasing that blockage so that the body can recover. If, however, you concentrate on disease as a physical symptom that can only be treated by medicine or surgery, then you are just continuing a process that is doomed to fail. Everyone should realise that the only alternative they have is to learn how they function at an energy level. They need to realise that they live in a world where life is fragile and that so much is often taken for granted. Society as a whole needs to evolve and transform the fears and anxieties that exist. We need to understand that we are in this world to evolve as spiritual beings.

As I stated earlier, the intelligence implicit in energy is phenomenal. When we cut our hair or nails, they automatically grow again, while every few months, every drop of blood in our bodies is renewed. The body is continuously renewing itself. Envision your life as that of a canvas. We are the painters and we have the control to paint whatever kind of life and experiences we wish. Paint the reality you want to paint. Clear off the canvas and start painting the life you want to experience. The best way to begin this process is to understand that you are made up of energy and that your body has phenomenal potential and infinite possibilities. The worst thing you can do is to be disconnected from that potential. This is because the consequence of the disconnection is that you will instead become connected with negative aspects of your life that will not make you function healthier or happier.

When we take control of the energy and speak internally to it in a positive manner, what we will see is change for the better because the body will reflect what is going on energetically. Understand that your emotions and mental perception have the ability to lead to illness if you let them. The time has come for people to either continue down a failed route, continue giving our symptoms different names, continue listening to multinational drug companies whose PR campaign want us to believe they are only around the corner from a cure, or we can simpl stop. We can forget the past and instead focus all of our time, effort and energy on our health. By doing so, we would be looking at a very productive and positive outcome. Let go of the fear that disease has to be something you will have for the rest of your life. I have never read in any book that we have to die or suffer because of illness.

Medical institutions control much of what you see and hear with regard to illness. Do not allow them to project a grim future for you. Take responsibility for your own future and allow your perception of what lies ahead to be a healthy and happy one. There is no reason why you cannot recover from any condition be it cancer, depression, etc. We are multidimensional beings with infinite possibilities. We have the ability to achieve whatever we want to achieve; the key is to unlock the courage and the strength to go for it.

Remember at the beginning of this book where I encouraged you to be your own flight archer and to go as far as you possibly could in life. It is essential that you now take a positive attitude towards your life and health as negativity must have no role in moulding your future. Now is the time to activate that advice. Stop using excuses for reasons not to do things, and instead make excuses to do things. There is no future in the past, in fact, there is no future, there is just this moment. You can change your life for the better by just imagining the possibility of you returning to health, being happy and content. Focus on the light not the darkness. Why? Because it all begins in your imagination.

REMEMBER

Energy is the web that unites all reality, and each one of us is made up of the same stuff as the universe.

In 2000 I had glandular fever. I felt tired and had no energy. I went to Michael O'Doherty and he had me back to normal in two weeks. I found Michael to be a very positive and effective motivational speaker with teams that I have managed and trained. My advice is to anyone who has health problems to have a look at Michael's success. You would be amazed.

David Fitzgerald

Clare goalkeeper, David Fitzgerald.

'Unfolding our extrasensory or psychic potential is the gateway for humanity to mature out of its present economic, ecological and spiritual crisis into a species which is capable of living at peace with itself and in harmony with the Earth and Universe.'

Michael O Doherty

WWW.PLEXUSBIO-ENERGY.COM

TEL: +353 (0)65 6841844